TO BE A FATHER

Other Books by ALVIN SCHWARTZ

TO BE A FATHER

STORIES
LETTERS
ESSAYS
POEMS
COMMENTS
AND PROVERBS
ON THE DELIGHTS AND DESPAIRS OF FATHERHOOD

SELECTED, WITH AN INTRODUCTION AND NOTES, BY

ALVIN SCHWARTZ

CROWN PUBLISHERS, INC., NEW YORK

Selection from A *Death in the Family* by James Agee. Copyright ©
1957 by James Agee Trust. Reprinted by permission of Grosset & Dun-
lap, Inc.

"Discovery of a Father" from *Sherwood Anderson's Memoirs* by
Sherwood Anderson. Copyright 1939 by Eleanor Anderson. Reprinted
by permission of Harold Ober Associates Incorporated.

"Miniature" from *For Partly Proud Parents* by Richard Armour.
Copyright 1950 by Richard Armour. Reprinted by permission of John
Schaffner.

"Fathers-in-Law" by Sholem Asch. Reprinted by permission of G. P.
Putnam's Sons from *Children of Abraham* by Sholem Asch. Copyright
1942 by Sholem Asch.

Comment on Father's Day by Dorothy Barclay. Copyright © 1955
by the New York Times Company. Reprinted by permission.

Selection from A *Firm Word or Two* by Nathaniel Benchley. Copy-
right © 1965 by Nathaniel Benchley. Published by the McGraw-Hill
Book Company. Used with permission of the publishers and *The New
Yorker*.

"Daughters" from *Golden Fleece* by William Rose Benét. Copyright 1923 William Rose Benét; copyright 1933, 1935 Dodd, Mead &
Company. Used with permission of the publishers.

"Happy Birthday" from *Seeing Things* by John Mason Brown. Copyright 1946 by the McGraw-Hill Publishing Company. Reprinted by
permission of the author.

"The Snob" by Morley Callaghan. Copyright © 1961 by Morley
Callaghan. Reprinted by permission of the Harold Matson Company,
Inc.

"Let's Not Talk About It Now" from *All the Year Around* by Robert
Coates. Copyright 1943 by Robert M. Coates. Reprinted by permission
of Harold Ober Associates Incorporated.

Letter by Richard Harding Davis dated October 24, 1915. Reprinted
with the permission of Charles Scribner's Sons from *Adventures and
Letters of Richard Harding Davis*, page 387, edited by Charles B.
Davis. Copyright 1917 by Charles Scribner's Sons; renewal copyright
1945 by Hope Harding Davis Kehrig.

"The Gift of Song" by Clarence Day. Copyright 1923 by Clarence
Day; renewed 1951 by Katherine B. Day. Reprinted from *Life with
Father* by Clarence Day by permission of Alfred A. Knopf, Inc.

iv

To my father
and my children

ACKNOWLEDGMENTS

I am deeply grateful to the authors, publishers, and literary agents who granted me permission to include copyrighted material in this anthology. I owe a great debt of gratitude to Barbara C. Schwartz, my wife, for her important contributions to the extensive research and voluminous correspondence on which this work is based. For their generous assistance, I thank the librarians at Princeton and Rutgers Universities, at the New York Library, and at the public libraries in Princeton and Trenton, New Jersey. For their advice and suggestions, I am grateful to Mildred Rabinow of the Child Study Association of America, to Herbert Michelman, my editor, and to Marilyn E. Marlow, my literary agent. Anthologists have countless debts also to other anthologists. Two beautiful collections of letters were of particular value: Evan Jones's *The Father: Letters to Sons and Daughters* and Alan C. Valentine's *Fathers to Sons*.

CONTENTS

INTRODUCTION

THE MORNING my first son was born I realized with a start how little I knew of what it was to be a father, even though I had been a father's son for twenty-eight years. Why my ignorance should have surprised me, I am not sure. Certainly in the period in which I was growing toward manhood I did not give very much thought to my father's life as a father. We lived in separate worlds and I had other things on my mind. The last thing I was interested in was what he could teach me. When it came to fatherhood, he cooperated fully and told me nothing. In fact, the only time he mentioned the subject was when I made him angry. Then with grim satisfaction he would announce that soon enough I would know what it was to be a father. And there he would leave it.

My first son is now eleven and he has a brother and two sisters, and I have learned much of what my father promised. In living my life as a father, I also have come to understand far more of his life, for all of us as fathers travel essentially the same path— from the time a child is born through the confusion and uncertainty of raising him to the sudden, empty discovery he no longer is a child to the time he marries and has children of his own. Moreover, the roles we play in our children's lives do not differ greatly. As my father did in my childhood, I now serve as companion, as teacher, as philosopher and oracle, as disciplinarian, as banker, even as rival and enemy. Inevitably, we also share many of the same reactions, concerns, and frustrations. My pride in my children, my dismay over their behavior, my despair over their costs, my hopes for their future, my desire to achieve through them what I cannot achieve myself—these clearly were my father's feelings, and, if literature and history are witness, they are the feelings of most fathers.

For all this, however, no man's fatherhood is precisely the

same as any other's. This certainly has been the case with my father's life and with mine. They have been different because we are not the same, nor are our children, nor are the circumstances that have shaped us. It is these differences, indeed, rather than the similarities, that make some fatherhoods memorable, others meaningless, and still others hell. It also is because of these differences that no man really can tell another how to be a father—how to teach wisely, punish fairly, love well, and do everything else that should be done. Although the experiences of other fathers may be helpful, in the end the way one learns these things is on his own by finding out what is best in his case, by making mistakes and trying not to repeat them. It is painful and it is inefficient, but there doesn't seem to be any other way.

This is not to say my father did not influence my fatherhood. By his example, he did so in a hundred ways, although I am sure he did not realize he was teaching and I certainly did not know I was learning. Even now there are times when I find myself dealing with my children just as he dealt with me when I was a child. When this happens, it is as if thirty years had disappeared and suddenly I am my father and my children are me. It is eerie.

As my two sons grow older, I often think that one day I would like to sit with them and explain why I raised them as I did and from this suggest how they, in turn, might do a better job with their children. But this is hardly the wisest course. For one thing, I would have difficulty explaining some of my behavior. For another, there actually is not a great deal to tell. In the end, they would be embarrassed and I would feel absurd. Perhaps the best I can do when the time comes is point out as briefly as possible that no man's life is ordinary, that every man's life is different, and that, like all fathers, they will have to find their own way—and then, once having spoken my mind, keep my peace and pray for the best.

In bringing together this collection, my hope has been to provide a sense of the scope, the variety, and the riches that make fatherhood the remarkable undertaking, the unique adventure it is. The material I have selected meets two objectives: it illustrates problems, opportunities, and roles most fathers share, and underscores the differences in personal qualities and circumstances that determine our relationship with our children.

As I read more and more of how others saw fatherhood, inevitably I journeyed backward in time to my own childhood, reliving moments long dead, then forward in time to my own fatherhood, seeing the present through fresh eyes, wondering about the future and what awaits me. Other readers also will make such journeys.

ALVIN SCHWARTZ

Princeton, New Jersey

NEW FATHER,
PROUD PARENT

Fá ther. One who has begotten a child.

WEBSTER'S NEW INTERNATIONAL DICTIONARY

He shall grow strong and straight.

CARL EWALD

from

MY LITTLE BOY/ MY BIG GIRL*

. . . THE FINCHES SING my thoughts away. I feel so happy, so green and so full of shoots. Over my head sits a little bird with beautifully shiny feathers, soulful eyes and vibrancy in his voice.

"Take spring when it comes, and rejoice . . . Take happiness when it comes, and rejoice . . . Take love when it comes, and rejoice . . ."

The sun shines, the anemones nod in the wind. The trees are budding while the worms burrow and the earth is full of eggs and seeds.

I bow to the law of God which is not the black priest's sinister: "Thou shalt, Thou shalt not . . ." but the finches' and the anemones': "You can, You may . . ." Here where everything is birth and spring I pray for the child which is being born to me.

He shall grow up among the people of the earth as the anemones here—with his feet in the soil and his face lifted high toward the brilliant sun. He shall grow strong and straight. He shall be a person with eyes and a person with power—one of those whom others envy and persecute and who bends the will of the people. May he be a gentleman of LIFE. May his curiosity be fathomless, like his courage, his passion, his love and his anger.

May he find God Eternal.

May he walk his own path and obey his own law. May he be quiet or cry out—not just nearsighted and barren.

May he die when he is no longer alive.

This I promise: I shall cast no shadow over his youth, nor

---

* Carl Ewald was a writer, a forester, a schoolmaster, and a parent in Denmark in the late nineteenth and early twentieth centuries.

break his spirit, nor make my old clothes over to fit him. I shall acknowledge him when he appears in the oddest garb and with the strangest speech.

I shall grant him his dreams, his women, his friends and his poetry. . . .

*   *

The night you were born, I ceased being my father's boy and became my son's father. That night I began a new life.

HENRY GREGOR FELSEN: from
LETTERS TO A TEEN-AGE SON

*   *

My day-old son is plenty scrawny,
His mouth is wide with screams, or yawny,
His ears seem larger than he's needing,
His nose is flat, his chin's receding,
His skin is very, very red,
He has no hair upon his head,
And yet I'm proud as proud can be,
To hear you say he looks like me.

RICHARD ARMOUR: MINIATURE

*   *

. . . I ask myself what this mystery is.

CARL EWALD

from

MY LITTLE BOY/ MY BIG GIRL

MY LITTLE BOY is in there. I must admit things are very slow. There is not much to him yet, and it will be a long while before my role as a father can go into effect.

So far he is rather irritating to me. Often he screams quite horribly which, according to his mother, is a sign of all remarkable physical and psychological qualities. I ought to be pleased and I am, even if sometimes I do long for the time when he will find more acceptable ways of displaying his prowess.

At times his screaming makes me quite unreasonable and I blow up. Then the mother of the wonder rises in all her splendor, repeats what she has already impressed on me a thousand times and asks finally: "Would you rather he were quiet and sickly?" Whereupon I retreat from the battle, silent and beaten.

A mother is a watchdog, a lioness, an idiot. So one mustn't reason with her.

My little boy is in the hands of the women but I do keep an eye on him, of course.

I have bought a handbook called *The Care of Your First Child.* Not because I intend to lift a finger in this respect personally— I never stick my nose into things which are none of my business and I can bide my time—but for the sake of keeping my hand on the throttle. And this proves to be highly desirable.

Of course, my little boy's mother also has her handbook. Of course, she intends to bring up the little creature according to the letter of the law. Of course, her tender heart constantly brings her to make the most dreadful mistakes.

For instance: He gets fed at regular intervals; but when he has screamed a while so that "a stone would melt" he is sometimes picked up and given extra attention. Thus as his screaming breaks off in the middle of a wail my suspicion is aroused. Why would a true male give up halfway? Suddenly I stand in the bedroom, tear him away from his mother's tender arms and throw him brutally back into the crib he ought never to have left.

Or whenever the aunts are there, naturally my little boy is picked up then to go from arm to arm and be admired and kissed both here and there, until I arrive on the scene. The noble ladies ask who I think I am since my child is too good for their kisses.

"I don't know anything about you," I answer, "thus I assume that you are all infected with the world's worst diseases."

The indignation rises—also in me.

"I shall buy you a chocolate baby you can lick to death," I say.

General consternation. The skirts rustle. They find no words for their rage, but I do for mine:

"Why didn't you ladies acquire a child of your own while there was still time?"

They insist that I have seen them for the last time. But I sigh for I know their lies. They swear to Heaven that it is only by a complete mishap that this wonderful baby was born to such a scoundrel as I. I only smile, because I know the truth.

Of course, we own no such stupefier as a cradle. My little boy sleeps in a decent bed. But when he disagrees with his mother about the suitable time for sleep he gets rocked and jiggled and sung to—in short, he is fooled into sleep.

Then I come raging along like a storm, emitting the most dreadful threats. I want to cut out the tongue of the offender, to bolt the bed to the floor so that not seven horses could rock it one inch. I want to tie the child into the bed.

Naturally, I am called in to see the first smile on my little boy's face. And I tell the womenfolk that such twitches in the young gentleman's face have nothing to do with joyful feelings about life, but are the signs of a neat little stomach-ache. For two weeks after such blasphemy my word counts for naught, of course. Altogether, I cannot deny that the relationship between my little boy's mother and me is rather cool at the present time.

But no matter. I have been prepared for that, and I have prepared her. Once during a quiet hour, when our little boy was but a thought in our lives, I delivered her from the handed-down illusion that the child brings the marriage partners closer together. On the contrary, the child is the only acceptable cause for strife in a well-ordered marriage.

And we are reconciled.

It occurs to her that I am not quite as much of a barbarian as she first thought. And I discover that, in a way, I have her to thank for my little boy. Then we have festive times at his bedside. But for me there is always something false about it. For—true as it is that I owe her gratitude and respect for love and friendship and all the good that may exist between man and woman—still, I know nothing yet about what kind of mother she will become.

I have seen the most sensible women go out of their minds over their children. And I am too intelligent not to know that a woman's ability to conceive and bear a child is no guarantee that she is able to rear it. And then when the child is a man child . . .

And my little boy is going to be a man.

Thus, I attend—second-hand—to my paternal duties while I bide the time when I can personally step in. I maintain a cold and skeptical attitude highly needed with the delirium reigning through the whole house. I am brusque, hot-headed, unresponsive and brutal.

But, in between, when nobody sees me, I peek at my little boy. At such times my eyes water and my soul softens; it becomes dumb like a mother's and, full of wonder, I ask myself what this mystery is.

Suppose they had—without my knowledge—placed another man's child in the crib in there—would I then . . .

My little boy is beginning to live.*

Carefully, stumbling now and then on his little knock-kneed legs, he makes his way over the paving-stones, looks at everything that there is to look at and bites at every apple, both those which are his due and those which are forbidden him.

---

* This selection was prepared by a different translator than those that precede it. It appeared in an edition entitled *My Little Boy* which was published in 1906. The other Ewald selections were published in 1962.

He is not a pretty child and is the more likely to grow into a fine lad. But he is charming.

His face can light up suddenly and become radiant; and he can look at you with quite cold eyes. He has a strong intuition and he is incorruptible. He has never yet bartered a kiss for barley-sugar. There are people whom he likes and people whom he dislikes. There is one who has long courted his favour indefatigably and in vain; and, the other day, he formed a close friendship with another who had not so much as said "Good-day" to him before he had crept into her lap and nestled there with glowing resolution.

He has a habit which I love.

When we are walking together and there is anything that impresses him, he lets go my hand for a moment. Then, when he has investigated the phenomenon and arrived at a result, I feel his little fist in mine again.

He has bad habits too.

He is apt, for instance, suddenly and without the slightest reason, to go up to people whom he meets in the street and hit them with his little stick. What is in his mind, when he does so, I do not know; and, so long as he does not hit me, it remains a matter between himself and the people concerned.

He has an odd trick of seizing big words in a grown-up conversation, storing them up for a while and then asking me for an explanation:

"Father," he says, "what is life?"

I give him a tap in his little stomach, roll him over on the carpet and conceal my emotion under a mighty romp. Then, when we sit breathless and tired, I answer, gravely:

"Life is delightful, my little boy. Don't you be afraid of it!"

*   *

I am absurdly enthusiastic about a certain youngster, and find it difficult to conceive of any child surpassing her in health or intelligence, in rosy cheeks or abounding hair. . . .

WILL DURANT

... let me tell you, Saunders, that's not a common thing in twins.

CHARLES DICKENS

from

THE COUPLE WHO DOTE
UPON THEIR CHILDREN

"IT'S A VERY extraordinary thing, Saunders," says Mr. Whiffler to the visitor, "but—you have seen our little babies, the—the— twins?" The friend's heart sinks within him as he answers, "Oh, yes—often." "Your talking of the Pyramids," says Mr. Whiffler, quite as a matter of course, "reminds me of the twins. It's a very extraordinary thing about those babies—what colour should you say their eyes were?" "Upon my word," the friend stammers, "I hardly know how to answer"—the fact being, that except as the friend does not remember to have heard of any departure from the ordinary course of nature in the instance of these twins, they might have no eyes at all for aught he has observed to the contrary. "You wouldn't say they were red, I suppose?" says Mr. Whiffler. The friend hesitates, and rather thinks they are; but inferring from the expression of Mr. Whiffler's face that red is not the colour, smiles with some confidence, and says, "No, no! very different from that." "What should you say to blue?" says Mr. Whiffler. The friend glances at him, and observing a different expression in his face, ventures to say, "I should say they *were* blue—a decided blue." "To be sure!" cries Mr. Whiffler, triumphantly, "I knew you would! But what should you say if I was to tell you that the boy's eyes are blue and the girl's hazel, eh?" "Impossible!" exclaims the friend, not at all knowing why it should be impossible. "A fact, notwithstanding," cries Mr. Whiffler; "and let me tell you, Saunders, *that's* not a common thing in twins, or a circumstance that'll happen every day."

*   *

FRIEND AND PROTECTOR

My father can lick your father.

UNKNOWN

. . . the hand lay strongly on his shoulder. . . .

JAMES AGEE

from

A DEATH IN THE FAMILY

WHENEVER THEY WALKED downtown and walked back home, in the evenings, they always began to walk more slowly, from about the middle of the viaduct, and as they came near this corner they walked more slowly still, but with purpose; and paused a moment, at the edge of the sidewalk; then, without speaking, stepped into the dark lot and sat down on the rock, looking out over the steep face of the hill and at the lights of North Knoxville. Deep in the valley an engine coughed and browsed; couplings settled their long chains, and the empty cars sounded like broken drums. A man came up the far side of the street, walking neither slow nor fast, not turning his head, as he paused, and quite surely not noticing them; they watched him until he was out of sight, and Rufus felt, and was sure that his father felt, that though there was no harm in the man and he had as good a right as they did to be there, minding his own business, their journey was interrupted from the moment they first saw him until they saw him out of sight. Once he was out of sight they realized more pleasure in their privacy than before; they really relaxed in it. They looked across the darkness at the lights of North Knoxville. They were aware of the quiet leaves above them, and looked into them and through them. They looked between the leaves into the stars. Usually on these evening waits, or a few minutes before going on home, Rufus' father smoked a cigarette through, and when it was finished, it was time to get up and go on home. But this time he did not smoke. Up to recently he had always said something about Rufus' being tired, when they were still about a block away from the corner; but lately he had not done

13

so, and Rufus realized that his father stopped as much because he wanted to, as on Rufus' account. He was just not in a hurry to get home, Rufus realized; and, far more important, it was clear that he liked to spend these few minutes with Rufus. Rufus had come recently to feel a quiet kind of anticipation of the corner, from the moment they finished crossing the viaduct; and, during the ten to twenty minutes they sat on the rock, a particular kind of contentment, unlike any other that he knew. He did not know what this was, in words or ideas, or what the reason was; it was simply all that he saw and felt. It was, mainly, knowing that his father, too, felt a particular kind of contentment, here, unlike any other, and that their kinds of contentment were much alike, and depended on each other. Rufus seldom had at all sharply the feeling that he and his father were estranged, yet they must have been, and he must have felt it, for always during these quiet moments on the rock a part of his sense of complete contentment lay in the feeling that they were reconciled, that there was really no division, no estrangement, or none so strong, anyhow, that it could mean much, by comparison with the unity that was so firm and assured, here. He felt that although his father loved their home and loved all of them, he was more lonely than the contentment of this family love could help; that it even increased his loneliness, or made it hard for him not to be lonely. He felt that sitting out here, he was not lonely; or if he was, that he felt on good terms with the loneliness; that he was a homesick man, and that here on the rock, though he might be more homesick than ever, he was well. He knew that a very important part of his well-being came of staying a few minutes away from home, very quietly, in the dark, listening to the leaves if they moved, and looking at the stars; and that his own, Rufus' own presence, was fully as indispensable to this well-being. He knew that each of them knew of the other's well-being, and of the reasons for it, and knew how each depended on the other, how each meant more to the other, in this most important of all ways, than anyone or anything else in the world; and that the best of this well-being lay in this mutual knowledge, which was neither concealed nor revealed. He knew these things very distinctly, but not, of course, in any such way as we have of suggesting them in words. There were no words, or even ideas, or formed emotions, of the kind that have been suggested here, no more in the man than in the boy child. These realizations moved clearly through the senses, the memory, the feelings, the mere feeling of the place they paused at, about a quarter of a mile from home, on a rock under a stray tree that had grown in the city, their feet on un-domesticated clay, facing north through the night over the Southern Railway tracks and over North Knoxville, towards the deeply folded small mountains and the Powell River Valley, and above them, the trembling lanterns of the universe, seeming so near, so intimate, that when air stirred the leaves and their hair, it seemed to be the breathing, the whispering of the stars. Sometimes on these evenings his father would hum a little and the humming would break open into a word or two, but he never finished even a part of a tune, for silence was even more pleasurable, and sometimes he would say a few words, of very little consequence, but would never seek to say much, or to finish what he was saying, or to listen for a reply; for silence again was even more pleasurable. Sometimes, Rufus had noticed, he would stroke the wrinkled rock and press his hand firmly against it; and sometimes he would put out his cigarette and tear and scatter it before it was half finished. But this time he was much quieter than ordinarily. They slackened their walking a little sooner than usual and walked a little more slowly, without a word, to the corner; and hesitated, before stepping off the sidewalk into the clay, purely for the luxury of hesitation; and took their place on the rock without breaking silence. As always, Rufus' father took off his hat and put it over the front of his bent knee, and as always, Rufus imitated him, but this time his father did not roll a cigarette. They waited while the man came by, intruding on their privacy, and disappeared, as someone nearly always did, and then relaxed sharply into the pleasure of their privacy; but this time Rufus' father did not hum, nor did he say anything, nor even touch the rock with his hand, but sat with his hands hung between his knees and looked out over North Knoxville, hearing the restive assemblage of the train; and after there had been silence for a while, raised his head and looked up into the leaves and between the leaves into the broad stars, not smiling, but with his eyes more calm and grave and his mouth strong and more quiet, than Rufus had ever seen his eyes and his mouth; and as he watched his father's face, Rufus felt his father's hand settle, without groping or clumsiness, on the top of his bare head: it took his forehead and smoothed it, and pushed the hair backward from his forehead, and held the back of his head while Rufus pressed his head backward against the firm hand, and, in reply to that pressure, clasped over his right ear and cheek, over the whole side of the head, and drew Rufus' head quietly and strongly against the sharp cloth that covered his father's body, through which Rufus could feel the breathing ribs; then relinquished him, and Rufus sat upright, while the hand lay strongly on his shoulder, and he saw that his father's eyes had become still more clear and grave and that the deep lines around his mouth were satisfied; and looked up at what his father was so steadily looking at, at the leaves which silently breathed and at the stars which beat like hearts. He heard a long, deep sigh break from his father, and then his father's abrupt voice: "*Well . . .*" and the hand lifted from him and they both stood up.

*   *

You could hardly tell that he was breathing.

OLIVER LA FARGE

from

The Brush of Wings

. . . A NASTY VIRUS swept through the combination play school and infant swimming class that the boy went to three days a week, and he, too, came down with it. The virus got its work in during a spell of northeasterly weather that kept the children indoors. Its course was predictable. It ran about a week, with several days of really high fever, stomach ache, and generalized aches and pains. Toward the end, there were likely to be nosebleeds. The local pediatrician was excellent. He told Clara what to expect; it was an unpleasant business but no cause for fear. All the same, it is thoroughly upsetting to feel one's child furiously hot with fever, to have him crying from what medical people call "discomfort," and to be unable to quiet him even with the proven magic of holding and rocking him.

On Wednesday evening, when Gerald came home, Clara told him with intense relief that the boy's temperature had dropped. He had eaten some gelatin. Gerald took a turn with him. He was cheerful, but unnaturally quiet. You could see how the child had lost weight; his eyes, as blue as his mother's, were too large for his face. His father thought him too beautiful, alarmingly so.

He had a nosebleed early Thursday morning. It was Clara who first heard his frightened call and went in to him. She was pretty well worn out by the days just past, and the sight of the rich bleeding was too much for her. Gerald took over, fully prepared to be late, to miss a morning or a day from work. He managed to get his son interested in the idea of the little pipes through which blood runs, one of which had broken and had to get well, and got him past the fear. He sold him on the cracked ice. The bleeding stopped soon enough for Gerald to eat breakfast at the usual time. He felt wrung out and was surprised at his appetite. He told Clara to telephone the doctor on general principles, as soon as he could be reached at his office, and went to work.

When Gerald came home that night, he found that there had been three more nosebleeds, none as severe as the first. Clara had dealt with them competently. She was haggard, and he began to worry lest she catch the bug, too. He took his turn with the boy. The fever had stayed down, although the child's face was still flushed. He ate some junket. Then he grew sleepy, and his father left him about seven. He did not think there would be more bleeding.

Gerald and Clara had a cocktail and ate dinner. Gerald prescribed a glass of claret apiece.

Shortly after eight, they went into the boy's room, found him drowsily awake, and gave him an aspirin tablet, the pink, lemony-tasting kind you have to hide lest children eat it as candy. It was important that he have it, to keep his fever down and insure his sleep. They also took his temperature, and were relieved that it was a hundred degrees even. Clara was easier than she had been when her husband came home, but still tense, and plainly done in. He told her to take a sleeping pill and go to bed; he had brought some work with him and would tackle that and listen for the boy. She resisted for no good reason, and then suddenly, gladly, gave in.

Gerald took his work up to the guest room, and left the door open and the nursery door open a crack. He set up a bridge table and started in on his papers. He was just well lost in the reading when the boy cried out. Gerald got up and went in to him, closing the nursery door and switching on a shaded, fifteen-watt bulb he had put into a fixture when the sickness started.

It was another nosebleed, not a bad one, but the boy must have been asleep and the blood had run into his throat, partly choking him, and he was frightened. Gerald's first concern was to quiet him. Clara's pill would be just about taking effect and he did not want her wakened. He and the boy rocked together in the rocking chair. It was an old chair with an irritating squeak to which his son was devoted. Clara had put a refilled ice bag in the washbasin in the bathroom, just in case. When the boy was calm, Gerald was able to leave him, sitting in the chair and holding Kleenex to his nose, long enough to run and get it. What a good little soldier the kid was, Gerald thought with a sudden, purely male pride as he came back to him; what a little man when the pinch came. He took the boy on his lap again, and, rocking, set a fold of the ice bag against the infantile little nose. The coolness of the bag in his hand made him sharply aware of the warmth of the room, which he found uncomfortable. The boy pushed the ice bag gently aside, leaned forward, and spat out a small amount of blood, which landed on Gerald's knee. Gerald reached for the tissues, wiped his knee, and set the ice bag in place again as the small head went back against the crook of his elbow. The incident struck him as funny. He took the piece of tissue the child had been holding, which showed a trace of blood, and gave him a fresh one.

The boy said softly, "Too much cold," and Gerald set the bag on the floor. The hand in which the boy had been holding the fresh Kleenex to his nose lowered slowly; the paper was unspotted. Both his hands went limp and his eyes closed. His body relaxed all over. Gerald had heard and read of children going to

sleep in their parents' arms, and had been disappointed that it
almost never happened with him; the child was too live, too
determined not to miss anything. Gerald felt a deep satisfaction
now.

After a moment or two, he felt the child's neck. It was cool;
it seemed much cooler than the room. He felt the hands, and the
ankles between the snug cuffs of the pajamas and the slippers;
they were chilly. Making a long arm, he got a blanket from the
bed. He kept on rocking, hearing at each backward swing the
unfriendly creak of the chair. He could see well by the weak
bulb now; but around everything, and especially around the
boy's face, was an overlay of shadow. You could hardly tell that
he was breathing. He looked pale, but that could be the light.
Gerald had never seen that face so limp. There were traces of
blood around the nostril that had bled, and below both nostrils
a little blood at the corners of the mouth, which had fallen open.
The dark lashes lay on the cheeks, and the shadow over the
eyelids.

Of course the aspirin, which to an infant of that age was a
powerful drug, had taken effect, all the more strongly for having
been held off. You would expect the child to be exhausted. The
nosebleeds had been predicted and were not excessive. Gerald
himself felt cold, although he was still conscious of the warmth
of the room. As the child reclined, his head slightly back, his
nostrils were more important than usual in his face. They had
an extraordinary quality of slackness; so had his lips, as though
the outlines of lips and nostrils had been fudged in the drawing.
Limp, a pervasive limpness, the eyelids and lashes, the nose, the
mouth, the whole body. He wanted to lift the blanket and look
at the hands, but could not. Those hands moved him too much.
He had thought it funny when the boy spat blood but perhaps
it was not. Where had that blood come from? For a moment he
felt himself swirl and sink.

There were two impossibilities. One was to perform any act
that did not belong in the normal process of quieting a child;
the other was to awaken Clara. He went on rocking slowly. It
was all very well that the various stages of this illness had been
predicted by the doctor; there is always the exception. What are
the effects of a hundred and four degrees of fever, not in the

evening but on waking in the morning? He had entered the
chain of reasoning along which he had to follow, knowing that
it led in perfect beauty to an end from which somehow he must
turn aside before he reached it. A detached part of his mind
stated clearly that this was pure emotion, tinged with an almost
literary element, but that recognition was theoretical and ineffec-
tual. Somewhere he had seen a face like this depicted. Or was
it carved? Painted, he thought. He had an unplaceable memory
of a picture of deathly relaxation. At the time, it had seemed
just bad, gruesome realism.

He set himself to rock a hundred times, counting. His heart
was beating too hard and too fast, in a way that was alarming
in itself and that aroused an ancient, feral certainty of danger.
His stomach was moist; there was sweat on his cold palms.
Eighteen, nineteen, twenty . . . His solitude was unutterable,
but that was required as he moved along the silent links of fear.
There was nothing to do but wait and find out, and it was for
him alone. The child did not stir. Thirty-five, thirty-six, thirty-
seven . . . There are wings in the room now, he thought bitterly
—the dreadful wings of the dark angel. He needed Clara to the
center of his bowels, and he thanked God she was not there.
The thought of the doctor never occurred to him. His counting
reached fifty.

At the seventy-sixth rock of the chair, the boy let his head fall
over, so his cheek lay on Gerald's arm. At ninety-one, he snored
once, and thereafter his breathing was strong and moderately
audible. With a giddy desire for laughter, Gerald realized that,
throughout the counting, his son's body had been snugly warm
against his. The seventeenth-century practice of blood-letting, he
thought with an inclination to giggle, combined with aspirin,
would produce a low temperature.

He tucked the sleeping infant into bed, stood for a moment
to watch and listen, and then left the room. He felt weak and
as if he had been cleansed throughout his body. He went downstairs, mixed a whiskey-and-soda, and settled down with the drink
and a smoke. The documents could go for this evening. In half
an hour he would check on the boy and go to bed. He felt as
if he had just completed a very important, difficult piece of work.
He felt extraordinarily at ease. He looked at his watch. He would

wait a full thirty minutes before looking in on his son, although he was magnificently sleepy.

*   *

For the first time I knew that I was the son of my father.

SHERWOOD ANDERSON
DISCOVERY OF A FATHER

ONE OF THE STRANGEST RELATIONSHIPS in the world is that between father and son. I know it now from having sons of my own.

A boy wants something very special from his father. You hear it said that fathers want their sons to be what they feel they cannot themselves be, but I tell you it also works the other way. I know that as a small boy I wanted my father to be a certain thing he was not. I wanted him to be a proud, silent, dignified father. When I was with other boys and he passed along the street, I wanted to feel a glow of pride: 'There he is. That is my father.'

But he wasn't such a one. He couldn't be. It seemed to me then that he was always showing off. Let's say someone in our town had got up a show. They were always doing it. The druggist would be in it, the shoe-store clerk, the horse-doctor, and a lot of women and girls. My father would manage to get the chief comedy part. It was, let's say, a Civil War play and he was a comic Irish soldier. He had to do the most absurd things. They thought he was funny, but I didn't.

I thought he was terrible. I didn't see how Mother could stand it. She even laughed with the others. Maybe I would have laughed if it hadn't been my father.

Or there was a parade, the Fourth of July or Decoration Day. He'd be in that, too, right at the front of it, as Grand Marshal or something, on a white horse hired from a livery stable.

He couldn't ride for shucks. He fell off the horse and everyone hooted with laughter, but he didn't care. He even seemed to like it. I remember once when he had done something ridiculous, and

right out on Main Street, too. I was with some other boys and
they were laughing and shouting at him and he was shouting back
and having as good a time as they were. I ran down an alley back
of some stores and there in the Presbyterian Church sheds I had
a good long cry.

Or I would be in bed at night and Father would come home a
little lit up and bring some men with him. He was a man who
was never alone. Before he went broke, running a harness shop,
there were always a lot of men loafing in the shop. He went
broke, of course, because he gave too much credit. He couldn't
refuse it and I thought he was a fool. I had got to hating him.

There'd be men I didn't think would want to be fooling around
with him. There might even be the superintendent of our schools
and a quiet man who ran the hardware store. Once I remember
there was a white-haired man who was a cashier of the bank. It
was a wonder to me they'd want to be seen with such a windbag.
That's what I thought he was. I know now what it was that
attracted them. It was because life in our town, as in all small
towns, was at times pretty dull and he livened it up. He made
them laugh. He could tell stories. He'd even get them to singing.

If they didn't come to our house, they'd go off, say, at night,
to where there was a grassy place by a creek. They'd cook food
there and drink beer and sit about listening to his stories.

He was always telling stories about himself. He'd say this or
that wonderful thing had happened to him. It might be something that made him look like a fool. He didn't care.

If an Irishman came to our house, right away Father would
say he was Irish. He'd tell what county in Ireland he was born in.
He'd tell things that happened there when he was a boy. He'd
make it seem so real that, if I hadn't known he was born in southern Ohio, I'd have believed him myself.

If it was a Scotchman the same thing happened. He'd get a
burr into his speech. Or he was a German or a Swede. He'd be
anything the other man was. I think they all knew he was lying,
but they seemed to like him just the same. As a boy that was
what I couldn't understand.

And there was Mother. How could she stand it? I wanted to
ask, but never did. She was not the kind you asked such questions.

I'd be upstairs in my bed, in my room above the porch, and

Father would be telling some of his tales. A lot of Father's stories were about the Civil War. To hear him tell it he'd been in about every battle. He'd known Grant, Sherman, Sheridan, and I don't know how many others. He'd been particularly intimate with General Grant so that when Grant went East, to take charge of all the armies, he took Father along.

'I was an orderly at headquarters and Sam Grant said to me, "Irve," he said, "I'm going to take you along with me." '

It seems he and Grant used to slip off sometimes and have a quiet drink together. That's what my father said. He'd tell about the day Lee surrendered, and how, when the great moment came, they couldn't find Grant.

'You know,' my father said, 'about General Grant's book, his memoirs. You've read of how he said he had a headache and how, when he got word that Lee was ready to call it quits, he was suddenly and miraculously cured.

'Huh,' said Father. 'He was in the woods with me.

'I was in there with my back against a tree. I was pretty well corned. I had got hold of a bottle of pretty good stuff.

'They were looking for Grant. He had got off his horse and come into the woods. He found me. He was covered with mud.

'I had the bottle in my hand. What'd I care? The war was over. I knew we had them licked.'

My father said that he was the one who told Grant about Lee. An orderly riding by had told him, because the orderly knew how thick he was with Grant. Grant was embarrassed.

'But, Irve, look at me. I'm all covered with mud,' he said to Father.

And then, my father said, he and Grant decided to have a drink together. They took a couple of shots and then, because he didn't want Grant to show up potted before the immaculate Lee, he smashed the bottle against the tree.

'Sam Grant's dead now and I wouldn't want it to get out on him,' my father said.

That's just one of the kind of things he'd tell. Of course the men knew he was lying, but they seemed to like it just the same.

When we got broke, down and out, do you think he ever brought anything home? Not he. If there wasn't anything to eat in the house, he'd go off visiting around at farmhouses. They all

wanted him. Sometimes he'd stay away for weeks, Mother working to keep us fed, and then home he'd come bringing, let's say,
a ham. He'd got it from some farmer friend. He'd slap it on the
table in the kitchen. 'You bet I'm going to see that my kids have
something to eat,' he'd say, and Mother would just stand smiling
at him. She'd never say a word about all the weeks and months
he'd been away, not leaving us a cent for food. Once I heard her
speaking to a woman in our street. Maybe the woman had dared
to sympathize with her. 'Oh,' she said, 'it's all right. He isn't ever
dull like most of the men in this street. Life is never dull when
my man is about.'

But often I was filled with bitterness, and sometimes I wished
he wasn't my father. I'd even invent another man as my father.
To protect my mother I'd make up stories of a secret marriage
that for some strange reason never got known. As though some
man, say, the president of a railroad company or maybe a Con-
gressman, had married my mother, thinking his wife was dead
and then it turned out she wasn't.

Now they had to hush it up, but I got born just the same. I
wasn't really the son of my father. Somewhere in the world there
was a very dignified, quite wonderful man who was really my
father. I even made myself half-believe these fancies.

And then there came a certain night. Mother was away from
home. Maybe there was a church that night. Father came in.
He'd been off somewhere for two or three weeks. He found me
alone in the house, reading by the kitchen table.

It had been raining and he was very wet. He sat and looked at
me for a long time, not saying a word. I was startled, for there
was on his face the saddest look I had ever seen. He sat for a
time, his clothes dripping. Then he got up.

'Come on with me,' he said.

I got up and went with him out of the house. I was filled with
wonder, but I wasn't afraid. We went along a dirt road that led
down into a valley, about a mile out of town, where there was a
pond. We walked in silence. The man who was always talking
had stopped his talking.

I didn't know what was up and had the queer feeling that I
was with a stranger. I don't know whether my father intended it
so. I don't think he did.

The pond was quite large. It was still raining hard and there were flashes of lightning followed by thunder. We were on a grassy bank at the pond's edge when my father spoke, and in the darkness and rain his voice sounded strange.

'Take off your clothes,' he said. Still filled with wonder, I began to undress. There was a flash of lightning and I saw that he was already naked.

Naked, we went into the pond. Taking my hand he pulled me in. It may be that I was too frightened, too full of a feeling of strangeness, to speak. Before that night my father had never seemed to pay any attention to me.

'And what is he up to now?' I kept asking myself. I did not swim very well, but he put my hand on his shoulder and struck out into the darkness.

He was a man with big shoulders, a powerful swimmer. In the darkness I could feel the movement of his muscles. We swam to the far edge of the pond and then back to where we had left our clothes. The rain continued and the wind blew. Sometimes my father swam on his back and when he did, he took my hand in his large powerful one and moved it over so that it rested always on his shoulder. Sometimes there would be a flash of lightning and I could see his face quite clearly.

It was as it was earlier, in the kitchen, a face filled with sadness. There would be the momentary glimpse of his face and then again the darkness, the wind and the rain. In me there was a feeling I had never known before.

It was a feeling of closeness. It was something strange. It was as though there were only we two in the world. It was as though I had been jerked suddenly out of myself, out of my world of the schoolboy, out of a world in which I was ashamed of my father.

He had become blood of my blood; the strong swimmer and I the boy clinging to him in the darkness. We swam in silence and in silence we dressed in our wet clothes, and went home.

There was a lamp lighted in the kitchen, and when we came in, the water dripping from us, there was my mother. She smiled at us. I remember that she called us 'boys.' 'What have you boys been up to?' she asked, but my father did not answer. As he had begun the evening's experience with me in silence, so he ended it. He turned and looked at me. Then he went, I thought, with a new and strange dignity, out of the room.

I climbed the stairs to my own room, undressed in darkness and got into bed. I couldn't sleep and did not want to sleep. For the first time I knew that I was the son of my father. He was a story-teller as I was to be. It may be that I even laughed a little softly there in the darkness. If I did, I laughed knowing that I would never again be wanting another father.

*   *

*It is not flesh and blood, but the heart
which makes us fathers and sons.*

JOHANN VON SCHILLER

*   *

*I began to sustain the illusion that he was I,
and therefore . . . that I was my father.*

E. B. WHITE
ONCE MORE TO THE LAKE

ONE SUMMER, along about 1904, my father rented a camp on a lake in Maine and took us all there for the month of August. We all got ringworm from some kittens and had to rub Pond's Extract on our arms and legs night and morning, and my father rolled over in a canoe with all his clothes on; but outside of that the vacation was a success and from then on none of us ever thought there was any place in the world like that lake in Maine. We returned summer after summer—always on August 1st for one month. I have since become a salt-water man, but sometimes in summer there are days when the restlessness of the tides and the fearful cold of the sea water and the incessant wind which blows across the afternoon and into the evening make me wish for the placidity of a lake in the woods. A few weeks ago this feeling got so strong I bought myself a couple of bass hooks and a spinner and returned to the lake where we used to go, for a week's fishing and to revisit old haunts.

I took along my son, who had never had any fresh water up his nose and who had seen lily pads only from train windows. On the journey over to the lake I began to wonder what it would be like. I wondered how time would have marred this unique, this holy spot—the coves and streams, the hills that the sun set behind, the camps and the paths behind the camps. I was sure that the tarred road would have found it out and I wondered in what other ways it would be desolated. It is strange how much you can remember about places like that once you allow your mind to return into the grooves which lead back. You remember one thing, and that suddenly reminds you of another thing. I guess I remembered clearest of all the early mornings, when the lake was cool and motionless, remembered how the bedroom smelled of the lumber it was made of and of the wet woods whose scent entered through the screen. The partitions in the camp were thin and did not extend clear to the top of the rooms, and as I was always the first up I would dress softly so as not to wake the others, and sneak out into the sweet outdoors and start out in the canoe, keeping close along the shore in the long shadows of the pines. I remembered being very careful never to rub my paddle against the gunwale for fear of disturbing the stillness of the cathedral.

The lake had never been what you would call a wild lake. There were cottages sprinkled around the shores, and it was in farming country although the shores of the lake were quite heavily wooded. Some of the cottages were owned by nearby farmers, and you would live at the shore and eat your meals at the farmhouse. That's what our family did. But although it wasn't wild, it was a fairly large and undisturbed lake and there were places in it which, to a child at least, seemed infinitely remote and primeval.

I was right about the tar: it led to within half a mile of the shore. But when I got back there, with my boy, and we settled into a camp near a farmhouse and into the kind of summertime I had known, I could tell that it was going to be pretty much the same as it had been before—I knew it, lying in bed the first morning, smelling the bedroom, and hearing the boy sneak quietly out and go off along the shore in a boat. I began to sustain the illusion that he was I, and therefore, by simple transposition, that I was my father. This sensation persisted, kept cropping up all the time we were there. It was not an entirely new feeling, but in this

setting it grew much stronger. I seemed to be living a dual existence. I would be in the middle of some simple act, I would be
picking up a bait box or laying down a table fork, or I would be
saying something, and suddenly it would be not I but my father
who was saying the words or making the gesture. It gave me a
creepy sensation.

We went fishing the first morning. I felt the same damp moss
covering the worms in the bait can, and saw the dragonfly alight
on the tip of my rod as it hovered a few inches from the surface
of the water. It was the arrival of this fly that convinced me beyond any doubt that everything was as it always had been, that
the years were a mirage and there had been no years. The small
waves were the same, chucking the rowboat under the chin as we
fished at anchor, and the boat was the same boat, the same color
green and the ribs broken in the same places, and under the
floor-boards the same fresh-water leavings and débris—the dead
helgramite, the wisps of moss, the rusty discarded fishhook, the
dried blood from yesterday's catch. We stared silently at the tips
of our rods, at the dragonflies that came and went. I lowered the
tip of mine into the water, tentatively, pensively dislodging the
fly, which darted two feet away, poised, darted two feet back, and
came to rest again a little farther up the rod. There had been no
years between the ducking of this dragonfly and the other one—
the one that was part of memory. I looked at the boy, who was
silently watching his fly, and it was my hands that held his rod,
my eyes watching. I felt dizzy and didn't know which rod I was
at the end of.

We caught two bass, hauling them in briskly as though they
were mackerel, pulling them over the side of the boat in a busi-
nesslike manner without any landing net, and stunning them
with a blow on the back of the head. When we got back for a
swim before lunch, the lake was exactly where we had left it, the
same number of inches from the dock, and there was only the
merest suggestion of a breeze. This seemed an utterly enchanted
sea, this lake you could leave to its own devices for a few hours
and come back to, and find that it had not stirred, this constant
and trustworthy body of water. In the shallows, the dark, water-
soaked sticks and twigs, smooth and old, were undulating in
clusters on the bottom against the clean ribbed sand, and the track

of the mussel was plain. A school of minnows swam by, each minnow with its small individual shadow, doubling the attendance, so clear and sharp in the sunlight. Some of the other campers were in swimming, along the shore, one of them with a cake of soap, and the water felt thin and clear and unsubstantial. Over the years there had been this person with the cake of soap, this cultist, and here he was. There had been no years.

Up to the farmhouse to dinner through the teeming, dusty field, the road under our sneakers was only a two-track road. The middle track was missing, the one with the marks of the hooves and the splotches of dried, flaky manure. There had always been three tracks to choose from in choosing which track to walk in; now the choice was narrowed down to two. For a moment I missed terribly the middle alternative. But the way led past the tennis court, and something about the way it lay there in the sun reassured me; the tape had loosened along the backline, the alleys were green with plantains and other weeds, and the net (installed in June and removed in September) sagged in the dry noon, and the whole place steamed with midday heat and hunger and emptiness. There was a choice of pie for dessert, and one was blueberry and one was apple, and the waitresses were the same country girls, there having been no passage of time, only the illusion of it as in a dropped curtain—the waitresses were still fifteen; their hair had been washed, that was the only difference— they had been to the movies and seen the pretty girls with the clean hair.

Summertime, oh summertime, pattern of life indelible, the fadeproof lake, the woods unshatterable, the pasture with the sweetfern and the juniper forever and ever, summer without end; this was the background, and the life along the shore was the design, the cottages with their innocent and tranquil design, their tiny docks with the flagpole and the American flag floating against the white clouds in the blue sky, the little paths over the roots of the trees leading from camp to camp and the paths leading back to the outhouses and the can of lime for sprinkling, and at the souvenir counters at the store the miniature birch-bark canoes and the post cards that showed things looking a little better than they looked. This was the American family at play, escaping the city heat, wondering whether the newcomers in the camp at the head of the cove were "common" or "nice," wondering whether it was true that the people who drove up for Sunday dinner at the farmhouse were turned away because there wasn't enough chicken.

It seemed to me, as I kept remembering all this, that those times and those summers had been infinitely precious and worth saving. There had been jollity and peace and goodness. The arriving (at the beginning of August) had been so big a business in itself, at the railway station the farm wagon drawn up, the first smell of the pine-laden air, the first glimpse of the smiling farmer, and the great importance of the trunks and your father's enormous authority in such matters, and the feel of the wagon under you for the long ten-mile haul, and at the top of the last long hill catching the first view of the lake after eleven months of not seeing this cherished body of water. The shouts and cries of the other campers when they saw you, and the trunks to be unpacked, to give up their rich burden. (Arriving was less exciting nowadays, when you sneaked up in your car and parked it under a tree near the camp and took out the bags and in five minutes it was all over, no fuss, no loud wonderful fuss about trunks.)

Peace and goodness and jollity. The only thing that was wrong now, really, was the sound of the place, an unfamiliar nervous sound of the outboard motors. This was the note that jarred, the one thing that would sometimes break the illusion and set the years moving. In those other summertimes all motors were inboard; and when they were at a little distance, the noise they made was a sedative, an ingredient of summer sleep. They were one-cylinder and two-cylinder engines, and some were make-and-break and some were jump-spark, but they all made a sleepy sound across the lake. The one-lungers throbbed and fluttered, and the twin-cylinder ones purred and purred, and that was a quiet sound too. But now the campers all had outboards. In the daytime, in the hot mornings, these motors made a petulant, irritable sound; at night, in the still evening when the afterglow lit the water, they whined about one's ears like mosquitoes. My boy loved our rented outboard, and his great desire was to achieve singlehanded mastery over it, and authority, and he soon learned the trick of choking it a little (but not too much), and the adjustment of the needle valve. Watching him I would remember the things you could do with the old one-cylinder engine with the heavy flywheel, how you could have it eating out of your hand if you got really close to it spiritually. Motor boats in those days didn't have clutches, and you would make a landing by shutting off the motor at the proper time and coasting in with a dead rudder. But there was a way of reversing them, if you learned the trick, by cutting the switch and putting it on again exactly on the final dying revolution of the flywheel, so that it would kick back against compression and begin reversing. Approaching a dock in a strong following breeze, it was difficult to slow up sufficiently by the ordinary coasting method, and if a boy felt he had complete mastery over his motor, he was tempted to keep it running beyond its time and then reverse it a few feet from the dock. It took a cool nerve, because if you threw the switch a twentieth of a second too soon you would catch the flywheel when it still had speed enough to go up past center, and the boat would leap ahead, charging bull-fashion at the dock.

We had a good week at the camp. The bass were biting well and the sun shone endlessly, day after day. We would be tired at night and lie down in the accumulated heat of the little bed-rooms after the long hot day and the breeze would stir almost imperceptibly outside and the smell of the swamp drift in through the rusty screens. Sleep would come easily and in the morning the red squirrel would be on the roof, tapping out his gay routine. I kept remembering everything, lying in bed in the mornings— the small steamboat that had a long rounded stern like the lip of a Ubangi, and how quietly she ran on the moonlight sails, when the older boys played their mandolins and the girls sang and we ate doughnuts dipped in sugar, and how sweet the music was on the water in the shining night, and what it had felt like to think about girls then. After breakfast we would go up to the store and the things were in the same place—the minnows in a bottle, the plugs and spinners disarranged and pawed over by the youngsters from the boys' camp, the Fig Newtons and the Bee-man's gum. Outside, the road was tarred and cars stood in front of the store. Inside, all was just as it had always been, except there was more Coca Cola and not so much Moxie and root beer and birch beer and sarsaparilla. We would walk out with a bottle of pop apiece and sometimes the pop would backfire up our noses and hurt. We explored the streams, quietly, where the turtles slid off the sunny logs and dug their way into the soft bottom;

and we lay on the town wharf and fed worms to the tame bass. Everywhere we went I had trouble making out which was I, the one walking at my side, the one walking in my pants.

One afternoon while we were there at that lake a thunderstorm came up. It was like the revival of an old melodrama that I had seen long ago with childish awe. The second-act climax of the drama of the electrical disturbance over a lake in America had not changed in any important respect. This was the big scene, still the big scene. The whole thing was so familiar, the first feeling of oppression and heat and a general air around camp of not wanting to go very far away. In midafternoon (it was all the same) a curious darkening of the sky, and a lull in everything that had made life tick; and then the way the boats suddenly swung the other way at their moorings with the coming of a breeze out of the new quarter, and the premonitory rumble. Then the kettle drum, then the snare, then the bass drum and cymbals, then crackling light against the dark, and the gods grinning and licking their chops in the hills. Afterward the calm, the rain steadily rustling in the calm lake, the return of light and hope and spirits, and the campers running out in joy and relief to go swimming in the rain, their bright cries perpetuating the deathless joke about how they were getting simply drenched, and the children screaming with delight at the new sensation of bathing in the rain, and the joke about getting drenched linking the generations in a strong indestructible chain. And the comedian who waded in carrying an umbrella.

When the others went swimming my son said he was going in too. He pulled his dripping trunks from the line where they had hung all through the shower, and wrung them out. Languidly, and with no thought of going in, I watched him, his hard little body, skinny and bare, saw him wince slightly as he pulled up around his vitals the small, soggy, icy garment. As he buckled the swollen belt suddenly my groin felt the chill of death.

*   *

I never thought our inseparable life could be separated. . . .

NICOLA SACCO
A LETTER TO HIS SON DANTE*

August 18, 1927. Charlestown State Prison

MY DEAR SON AND COMPANION:

Since the day I saw you last I had always the idea to write you this letter, but the length of my hunger strike and the thought I might not be able to explain myself, made me put it off all this time.

The other day, I ended my hunger strike and just as soon as I did that I thought of you to write to you, but I find that I did not have enough strength and I cannot finish it at one time. However, I want to get it down in any way before they take us again to the death house, because it is my conviction that just as soon as the court refuses a new trial to us they will take us there. And between Friday and Monday, if nothing happens, they will electrocute us right after midnight, on August 22nd. Therefore, here I am, right with you with love and with open heart as ever I was yesterday.

I never thought that our inseparable life could be separated, but the thought of seven dolorous years makes it seem it did come, but then it has not changed really the unrest and the heartbeat of affection. That has remained as it was. More. I say that our ineffable affection reciprocal, is today more than any other time, of course. That is not only a great deal but it is grand because you can see the real brotherly love, not only in joy but also and more in the struggle of suffering. Remember this, Dante. We have demonstrated this, and modesty apart we are proud of it.

Much we have suffered during this long Calvary. We protest today as we protested yesterday. We protest for our freedom.

If I stopped hunger strike the other day, it was because there was no more sign of life in me. Because I protested with my hunger strike yesterday as today I protest for life and not for death.

---

* In July, 1921, Nicola Sacco and Bartolomeo Vanzetti were convicted of the murder of a paymaster and a guard and the theft of $15,000 from a shoe company in South Braintree, Mass. Many believed that Sacco and Vanzetti were innocent of these crimes, that they had been convicted because they were political anarchists in a period in which there was strong antiradical sentiment in the United States. Persons throughout the world rallied to the support of the two men. But after six years of unsuccessful appeals, they were executed on August 22, 1927, four days after this letter was written to his thirteen-year-old son.

I sacrificed because I wanted to come back to the embrace of your dear little sister Ines and your mother and all the beloved friends and comrades of life and not death. So Son, today life begins to revive slow and calm, but yet without horizon and always with sadness and visions of death.

Well, my dear boy, after your mother had talked to me so much and I had dreamed of you day and night, how joyful it was to see you at last. To have talked with you like we used to in the days—in those days. Much I told you on that visit and more I wanted to say, but I saw that you will remain the same affectionate boy, faithful to your mother who loves you so much, and I did not want to hurt your sensibilities any longer, because I am sure that you will continue to be the same boy and remember what I have told you. I know that and what here I am going to tell you will touch your sensibilities, but don't cry Dante, because many tears have been wasted, as your mother's have been wasted for seven years, and never did any good. So, Son, instead of crying, be strong, so as to be able to comfort your mother, and when you want to distract your mother from the discouraging soulness, I will tell you what I used to do. To take her for a long walk in the quiet country, gathering wild flowers here and there, resting under the shade of trees, between the harmony of the vivid stream and the gentle tranquility of the mother-nature [sic], and I am sure that she will enjoy this very much, as you surely would be happy for it. But remember always, Dante, in the play of happiness, don't use all for yourself only, but down yourself just one step, at your side and help the weak ones that cry for help, help the prosecuted and the victim, because that are your better friends; they are the comrades that fight and fall as your father and Bartolo fought and fell yesterday for the conquest of the joy of freedom for all and the poor workers. In this struggle of life you will find more love and you will be loved.

I am sure that from what your mother told me about what you said during these terrible days when I was lying in the iniquitous death-house—that description gave me happiness because it showed you will be the beloved boy I had always dreamed.

Therefore, whatever should happen tomorrow, nobody knows, but if they should kill us, you must not forget to look at your friends and comrades with the smiling gaze of gratitude as you look at your beloved ones, because they love you as they love every one of the fallen persecuted comrades. I tell you, your father that is all the life to you, your father that loved you and saw them, and knows their noble faith (that is mine) their supreme sacrifice that they are still doing for our freedom, for I have fought with them, and they are the ones that still hold the last of our hope that today they can still save us from electrocution, it is the struggle and fight between the rich and the poor for safety and freedom, Son, which you will understand in the future of your years to come, of this unrest and struggle of life's death.

Much I thought of you when I was lying in the death-house—the singing, the kind tender voices of the children from the playground, where there was all the life and the joy of liberty—just one step from the wall which contains the buried agony of three buried souls. It would remind me so often of you and your sister Ines, and I wish I could see you every moment. But I feel better that you did not come to the death-house so that you could not see the horrible picture of three lying in agony to be electrocuted, because I do not know what effect it would have on your young age. But then, in another way if you were not so sensitive it would be very useful to you tomorrow when you could use this horrible memory to hold up to the world the shame of the country in this cruel persecution and unjust death. Yes, Dante, they can crucify our bodies today as they are doing, but they cannot destroy our ideas, that will remain for the youth of the future to come.

Dante, when I said three human lives buried, I meant to say that with us there is another young man by the name of Celestino Maderios that is to be electrocuted at the same time with us. He has been twice before in that horrible death-house, that should be destroyed with the hammers of real progress—that horrible house that will shame forever the future of the citizens of Massachusetts. They should destroy that house and put up a factory or school, to teach many of the hundreds of the poor orphan boys of the world.

Dante, I say once more to love and be nearest your mother and the beloved ones in these sad days, and I am sure that with your brave heart and kind goodness they will feel less discomfort. And you will also not forget to love me a little for I do—O, Sonny! thinking so much and so often of you.

Best fraternal greetings to the beloved ones, love and kisses to your little Ines and mother. Most hearty affectionate embrace.

Your Father and Companion

P.S. Bartolo sends you the most affectionate greetings. I hope that your years to come, of this unrest and struggle of life's death.
have written much better and more simple, if I was feeling good. But I am so weak.

*   *

She never fell from a horse in her life.
WILLIAM ALLEN WHITE
Obituary for His Daughter Mary*

May 17, 1921.

The Associated Press reports carrying the news of Mary White's death declared that it came as the result of a fall from a horse. How she would have hooted at that! She never fell from a horse in her life. Horses have fallen on her and with her—"I'm always trying to hold 'em in my lap," she used to say. But she was proud of few things, and one of them was that she could ride anything that had four legs and hair. Her death resulted not from a fall but from a blow on the head which fractured her skull, and the blow came from the limb of an overhanging tree on the parking.

The last hour of her life was typical of its happiness. She came home from a day's work at school, topped off by a hard grind with the copy on the High School Annual, and felt that a ride would refresh her. She climbed into her khakis, chattering to her mother about the work she was doing, and hurried to get her horse and be out on the dirt roads for the country air and the radiant green fields of the spring. As she rode through the town on an easy gallop, she kept waving at passers-by. She knew everyone in town. For a decade the little figure in the long pigtail and the red hair ribbon has been familiar on the streets of Emporia, and she got in the way of speaking to those who nodded at her. She passed the Kerrs, walking the horse in front of the Normal Library, and waved at them; passed another friend a few hundred feet farther on, and waved at her.

The horse was walking, and as she turned into North Merchant Street she took off her cowboy hat, and the horse swung into a lope. She passed the Tripletts and waved her cowboy hat at them, still moving gayly north on Merchant Street. A *Gazette* carrier

---

* William Allen White was editor of the Emporia, Kansas *Gazette*, where this memorial first was published.

passed—a High School boy friend—and she waved at him, but with her bridle hand; the horse veered quickly, plunged into the parking where the low-hanging limb faced her and, while she still looked back waving, the blow came. But she did not fall from the horse; she slipped off, dazed a bit, staggered, and fell in a faint. She never quite recovered consciousness.

But she did not fall from the horse, neither was she riding fast. A year or so ago she used to go like the wind. But that habit was broken, and she used the horse to get into the open, to get fresh, hard exercise, and to work off a certain surplus energy that welled up in her and needed a physical outlet. The need has been in her heart for years. It was back of the impulse that kept the dauntless little brown-clad figure on the streets and country roads of the community and built into a strong, muscular body what had been a frail and sickly frame during the first years of her life. But the riding gave her more than a body. It released a gay and hardy soul. She was the happiest thing in the world. And she was happy because she was enlarging her horizon. She came to know all sorts and conditions of men; Charley O'Brien, the traffic cop, was one of her best friends. W. L. Holtz, the Latin teacher, was another. Tom O'Connor, farmer-politician, and the Rev. J. H. Rice, preacher and police judge, and Frank Beach, music master, were her special friends; and all the girls, black and white, above the track and below the track, in Pepville and Stringtown, were among her acquaintances. And she brought home riotous stories of her adventures. She loved to rollick; persiflage was her natural expression at home. Her humor was a continual bubble of joy. She seemed to think in hyperbole and metaphor. She was mischievous without malice, as full of faults as an old shoe. No angel was Mary White, but an easy girl to live with for she never nursed a grouch five minutes in her life.

With all her eagerness for the out-of-doors, she loved books. On her table when she left her room were a book by Conrad, one by Galsworthy, "Creative Chemistry" by E. S. Slosson, and a Kipling book. She read Mark Twain, Dickens and Kipling before she was ten—all of their writings. Wells and Arnold Bennett particularly amused and diverted her. She was entered as a student in Wellesley for 1922; was assistant editor of the High School Annual this year, and in line for election to the editorship next

year. She was a member of the executive committee of the High
School Y.W.C.A.

Within the last two years she had begun to be moved by an
ambition to draw. She began as most children do by scribbling in
her school books, funny pictures. She bought cartoon magazines
and took a course—rather casually, naturally, for she was, after
all, a child with no strong purposes—and this year she tasted the
first fruits of success by having her pictures accepted by the High
School Annual. But the thrill of delight she got when Mr. Ecord,
of the Normal Annual, asked her to do the cartooning for that
book this spring, was too beautiful for words. She fell to her work
with all her enthusiastic heart. Her drawings were accepted, and
her pride—always repressed by a lively sense of the ridiculous figure she was cutting—was a really gorgeous thing to see. No suc-
cessful artist ever drank a deeper draft of satisfaction than she
took from the little fame her work was getting among her school-
fellows. In her glory, she almost forgot her horse—but never her
car.

For she used the car as a jitney bus. It was her social life. She
never had a "party" in all her nearly seventeen years—wouldn't
have one; but she never drove a block in her life that she didn't
begin to fill the car with pick-ups! Everybody rode with Mary
White—white and black, old and young, rich and poor, men and
women. She liked nothing better than to fill the car with long-
legged High School boys and an occasional girl, and parade the
town. She never had a "date," nor went to a dance, except once
with her brother Bill, and the "boy proposition" didn't interest
her—yet. But young people—great spring-breaking, varnish-crack-
ing, fender-bending, door-sagging carloads of "kids"—gave her
great pleasure. Her zests were keen. But the most fun she ever had
in her life was acting as chairman of the committee that got up
the big turkey dinner for the poor folks at the county home; scores
of pies, gallons of slaw, jam, cakes, preserves, oranges, and a
wilderness of turkey were loaded into the car and taken to the
county home. And, being of a practical turn of mind, she risked
her own Christmas dinner to see that the poor folks actually got
it all. Not that she was a cynic; she just disliked to tempt folks.
While there, she found a blind colored uncle, very old, who could

do nothing but make rag rugs, and she rustled up from her school friends rags enough to keep him busy for a season. The last engagement she tried to make was to take the guests at the county home out for a car ride. And the last endeavor of her life was to try to get a rest room for colored girls in the High School. She found one girl reading in the toilet, because there was no better place for a colored girl to loaf, and it inflamed her sense of injustice and she became a nagging harpy to those who she thought could remedy the evil. The poor she always had with her and was glad of it. She hungered and thirsted for righteousness; and was the most impious creature in the world. She joined the church without consulting her parents, not particularly for her soul's good. She never had a thrill of piety in her life, and would have hooted at a "testimony." But even as a little child, she felt the church was an agency for helping people to more of life's abundance, and she wanted to help. She never wanted help for herself. Clothes meant little to her. It was a fight to get a new rig on her; but eventually a harder fight to get it off. She never wore a jewel and had no ring but her High School class ring and never asked for anything but a wrist watch. She refused to have her hair up, though she was nearly seventeen. "Mother," she protested, "you don't know how much I get by with, in my braided pigtails, that I could not with my hair up." Above every other passion of her life was her passion not to grow up, to be a child. The tomboy in her, which was big, seemed loath to be put away forever in skirts. She was a Peter Pan who refused to grow up.

Her funeral yesterday at the Congregational Church was as she would have wished it; no singing, no flowers except the big bunch of red roses from her brother Bill's Harvard classmen—heavens, how proud that would have made her!—and the red roses from the *Gazette* forces, in vases, at her head and feet. A short prayer: Paul's beautiful essay on "Love" from the Thirteenth Chapter of First Corinthians; some remarks about her democratic spirit by her friend, John H. J. Rice, pastor and police judge, which she would have deprecated if she could; a prayer sent down for her by her friend, Carl Nau; and, opening the service, the slow, poignant movement from Beethoven's *Moonlight Sonata*, which she loved; and closing the service a cutting from the joyously melancholy first movement of Tchaikovsky's *Pathetic Symphony*, which she liked to hear, in certain moods, on the phonograph; then the Lord's Prayer by her friends in High School.

That was all.

For her pallbearers only her friends were chosen: her Latin teacher, W. L. Holtz; her High School principal, Rice Brown; her doctor, Frank Foncannon; her friend, W. W. Finney; her pal at the *Gazette* office, Walter Hughes; and her brother Bill. It would have made her smile to know that her friend, Charley O'Brien, the traffic cop, had been transferred from Sixth and Commercial to the corner near the church to direct her friends who came to bid her good-by.

A rift in the clouds in a gray day threw a shaft of sunlight upon her coffin as her nervous, energetic little body sank to its last sleep. But the soul of her, the glowing, gorgeous, fervent soul of her, surely was flaming in eager joy upon some other dawn.

TEACHER

You have to dig deep to bury your Daddy.

GYPSY PROVERB

. . . TO A SON

. . . I do not expect you to stand first. . . .

THEODORE ROOSEVELT

from

A LETTER TO HIS SON TED

Oyster Bay, May 7, 1901

BLESSED TED:

It was the greatest fun seeing you, and I really had a satisfactory time with you, and came away feeling that you were doing well. I am entirely satisfied with your standing, both in your studies and in athletics. I want you to do well in your sports, and I want even more to have you do well with your books; but I do not expect you to stand first in either, if so to stand could cause you overwork and hurt your health. I always believe in going hard at everything, whether it is Latin or mathematics, boxing or football, but at the same time I want to keep the sense of proportion. It is never worth while to absolutely exhaust one's self or to take big chances unless for an adequate object. I want you to keep in training the faculties which would make you, if the need arose, able to put your last ounce of pluck and strength into a contest. But I do not want you to squander these qualities. To have you play football as well as you do, and make a good name in boxing and wrestling, and be cox of your second crew, and stand second or third in your class in the studies, is all right. I should be rather sorry to see you drop too near the middle of your class, because, as you cannot enter college until you are nineteen, and will therefore be a year later in entering life, I want you to be prepared in the best possible way, so as to make up for the delay. But I know that all you can do you will do to keep substantially the position in the class that you have so far kept, and I have entire trust in you, for you have always deserved it. . . .

*   *

When I said I couldn't sing, he said nonsense.

CLARENCE DAY

from

LIFE WITH FATHER: "THE GIFT OF SONG"

ONE DAY when I was about ten years old, and George eight, Father suddenly remembered an intention of his to have us taught music. There were numerous other things that he felt every boy ought to learn, such as swimming, blacking his own shoes, and book-keeping; to say nothing of school work, in which he expected a boy to excel. He now recalled that music, too, should be included in our education. He held that all children should be taught to play on something, and sing.

He was right, perhaps. At any rate, there is a great deal to be said for his program. On the other hand, there are children and children. I had no ear for music.

Father was the last man to take this into consideration, however: he looked upon children as raw material that a father should mold. When I said I couldn't sing, he said nonsense. He went to the piano. He played a scale, cleared his throat, and sang *Do, re, mi,* and the rest. He did this with relish. He sang it again, high and low. He then turned to me and told me to sing it, too, while he accompanied me.

I was bashful. I again told him earnestly that I couldn't sing. He laughed. "What do *you* know about what you can or can't do?" And he added in a firm, kindly voice, "Do whatever I tell you." He was always so sure of himself that I couldn't help having faith in him. For all I knew, he could detect the existence of organs in a boy of which that boy had no evidence. It was astonishing, certainly, but if he said I could sing, I could sing.

I planted myself respectfully before him. He played the first note. He never wasted time in explanations; that was not his way; and I had only the dimmest understanding of what he wished me to do. But I struck out, haphazard, and chanted the extraordinary syllables loudly.

"No, no, no!" said Father, disgustedly.

We tried it again.

"No, no, no!" He struck the notes louder.

We tried it repeatedly. . . .

I gradually saw that I was supposed to match the piano, in some way, with my voice. But how such a thing could be done I had no notion whatever. The kind of sound a piano made was different from the sound of a voice. And the various notes—I could hear that each one had its own sound, but that didn't help me out any: they were all total strangers. One end of the piano made deep noises, the other end shrill! I could make my voice deep, shrill, or medium; but that was the best I could do.

At the end of what seemed to me an hour, I still stood at attention, while Father still tried energetically to force me to sing. It was an absolute deadlock. He wouldn't give in, and I couldn't. Two or three times I had felt for a moment I was getting the hang of it, but my voice wouldn't do what I wanted; I don't think it could. Anyhow, my momentary grasp of the problem soon faded. It felt so queer to be trying to do anything exact with my voice. And Father was so urgent about it, and the words so outlandish. *Do, re, mi, fa, sol, la, ti, do!* What a nightmare! though by this time he had abandoned his insistence on my learning the scale; he had reduced his demands to my singing one single note: *Do.* I continually opened my mouth wide, as he had instructed me, and shouted the word *Do* at random, hoping it might be the pitch. He snorted, and again struck the piano. I again shouted *Do.*

George sat on the sofa by the parlor door, watching me with great sympathy. He always had the easy end of it. George was a good brother; he looked up to me, loved me, and I couldn't help loving him; but I used to get tired of being his path-breaker in encounters with Father. All Father's experience as a parent was obtained at my hands. He was a man who had many impossible hopes for his children, and it was only as he tried these on me that he slowly became disillusioned. He clung to each hope tenaciously; he surrendered none without a long struggle; after which he felt baffled and indignant, and I felt done up, too. At such times if only he had repeated the attack on my brothers, it might have been hard on them but at least it would have given me a slight rest. But no, when he had had a disappointment, he turned to new projects. And as I was the eldest, the new were always tried out on me. George and the others trailed along happily, in comparative peace, while I perpetually confronted Father in a wrestling match upon some new ground. . . .

Mother came into the room in her long swishing skirts. Father was obstinately striking the piano for the nine thousandth time, and I was steadily though hopelessly calling out *Do*.

"Why Clare! What *are* you doing?" Mother cried.

Father jumped up. I suppose that at heart he was relieved at her interruption—it allowed him to stop without facing the fact of defeat. But he strongly wished to execute any such maneuver without loss of dignity, and Mother never showed enough regard for this, from his point of view. Besides, he was full of a natural irritation at the way things resisted him. He had visited only a part of this on me. The rest he now hurled at her. He said would she kindly go away and leave him alone with his sons. He declared he would not be interfered with. He banged the piano lid shut. He said he was "sick and tired of being systematically thwarted and hindered," and he swore he would be damned if he'd stand it. Off he went to his room.

"You'll only have to come right back down again," Mother called after him. "The soup's being put on the table."

"I don't want any dinner."

"Oh Clare! Please! it's oyster soup!"

"Don't want any." He slammed his room door.

We sat down, frightened, at table. I was exhausted. But the soup was a life-saver. It was more like a stew, really. Rich milk, oyster juice, and big oysters. I put lots of small hard crackers in mine, and one slice of French toast. That hot toast soaked in soup was delicious, only there wasn't much of it, and as Father particularly liked it, we had to leave it for him. But here was plenty of soup: a great tureen full. Each boy had two helpings.

Father came down in the middle of it, still offended, but he ate his full share. I guess he was somewhat in need of a life-saver himself. The chops and peas and potatoes came on. He gradually forgot how we'd wronged him.

There were too many things always happening at our family

dinners, too many new vexations, or funny things, for him to dwell on the past.

But though he was willing enough, usually, to drop small resentments, nevertheless there were certain recollections that remained in his mind—such as the feeling that Mother sometimes failed to understand his plans for our welfare, and made his duty needlessly hard for him by her interference; and the impression that I was an awkward little boy, and great trouble to train.

Not that these thoughts disturbed him, or lessened at all his self-confidence. He lit his cigar after dinner and leaned back philosophically, taking deep vigorous puffs with enjoyment, and drinking black coffee. When I said, "Good night, Father," he smiled at me like a humorous potter, pausing to consider—for the moment—an odd bit of clay. Then he patted me affectionately on the shoulder and I went up to bed.

*　　*

Life is hard; be steel; be a rock.

CARL SANDBURG

from

THE PEOPLE, YES

A father sees a son nearing manhood.
What shall he tell that son?
"Life is hard; be steel; be a rock."
And this might stand him for the storms
and serve him for humdrum and monotony
and guide him amid sudden betrayals
and tighten him for slack moments.
"Life is a soft loam; be gentle; go easy."
And this too might serve him.
Brutes have been gentled where lashes failed.
The growth of a frail flower in a path up

has sometimes shattered and split a rock.
A tough will counts. So does desire.
So does a rich soft wanting.
Without rich wanting nothing arrives.
Tell him too much money has killed men
and left them dead years before burial:
the quest of lucre beyond a few easy needs
has twisted good enough men
sometimes into dry thwarted worms.
Tell him time as a stuff can be wasted.
Tell him to be a fool every so often
and to have no shame over having been a fool
yet learning something out of every folly
hoping to repeat none of the cheap follies
thus arriving at intimate understanding
of a world numbering many fools.
Tell him to be alone often and get at himself
and above all tell himself no lies about himself
whatever the white lies and protective fronts
he may use amongst other people.
Tell him solitude is creative if he is strong
and the final decisions are made in silent rooms.
Tell him to be different from other people
if it comes natural and easy being different.
Let him have lazy days seeking his deeper motives.
Let him seek deep for where he is a born natural.
  Then he may understand Shakespeare
  and the Wright brothers, Pasteur, Pavlov,
  Michael Faraday and free imaginations
bringing changes into a world resenting change.
  He will be lonely enough
  to have time for the work
  he knows as his own.

*   *

My reliance is on your character. . . .

CHARLES SEDGWICK

from

A LETTER TO HIS SON CHARLES, JR.*

Lenox, September 19, 1837

. . . I SHOULD have answered your letter before, but I have not before today been in possession of ten dollars, which I enclose to you with pleasure. You do not say what you want it for, but I send it to you that you may have the option of declining to use it. I consider it one of the greatest uses for money for a young person to have it, and yet from sense, judgment and principle, to resist those temptations to which the young generally yield. Perhaps you will think the sum rather too small to give dignity to this moral, but to tell you the truth it is half I have, and the residue I want today. I think I can safely promise to procure and forward for your use all that you express a deliberate wish to have. I do not mean to go half way with you in my confidence. My *reliance* is on your character, your generous and disinterested disposition, your confidence in my affection, your determination to do the right thing, knowing my circumstances, and that there is nothing that I wish to conceal from you. It is, if not my greatest, certainly one of my greatest pleasures to believe your virtue is strong, that it is not dependent so much on the guardianship and vigilance of your friends, as on your own clear apprehension of right and your fixed principles.

---

* A cultured man of modest means, Charles Sedgwick was a county clerk in western Massachusetts during the first half of the nineteenth century. This letter to his sixteen-year-old son was written when the boy was living away from home at school.

*   *

*. . . you seem not far different from
what I was myself at your age. . . .*

WILLIAM CARLOS WILLIAMS
A LETTER TO HIS SON WILLIAM*

March 13, 1935

DEAREST BILL:

This I can say for certain, you seem not far different from what I was myself at your age. I don't mind saying I went through hell, what with worrying about my immortal soul and my hellish itch to screw almost any female I could get my hands on—which I never did. I can tell you it is almost as vivid today as it was then when I hear you speak of it. Everything seems upside down and one's self the very muck under one's foot.

It comes from many things, my dear boy, but mostly from the inevitable maladjustment consequent upon growing up in a more or less civilized environment. Any bum on the street, any crook who is his own master at the expense of the law is happier than the man who is trying to mould himself to a society which revolts his entire manhood. We do not want to fit into anything, we want to be free, potent, self-reliant—and that society cannot and will not permit. Nor would we be really satisfied if we found ourselves antisocial in our success. That is the situation of the great fortunes, the Morgans, the Vanderbilts, as well as the Al Capones of the world. They are "free" but at a terrific cost.

But more immediately, your difficulties arise from a lack of balance in your daily life, a lack of balance which has to be understood and withstood—for it cannot be avoided for the present. I refer to the fact that your intellectual life, for the moment, has eclipsed the physical life, the animal life, the normal he-man life, which every man needs and craves. If you were an athlete, a powerful body, one who could be a hero on the field or the diamond, a *Big* Hero, many of your mental torments would be lulled to sleep. But you cannot be that—so what? You'll have to wait and take it by a different course.

And after all, the athletes haven't it as easy as it seems. They may be soothed during the difficult years, but they've got to face the music some day, and that some day may be too late. They can't always be physical figures, and when the real test comes later, they often fold up and disappear completely.

---

* William Eric Williams was in his senior year at Williams College when he received this letter.

You, dear Bill, have a magnificent opportunity to enjoy life ahead of you. You have sensibility (even if it drives you nuts at times), which will be the source of keen pleasures later and the source of useful accomplishments too. You've got a brain, as you have been told *ad nauseam*. But these are the very things which are tormenting you, the very things which are your most valued possessions and which will be your joy tomorrow. Sure you are sentimental, sure you admire a man like Wordsworth and his "Tintern Abbey." It is natural, it is the correct reaction of your age in life. It is also a criticism of Wordsworth as you will see later. All I can say about that is, wait! Not wait cynically, idly, but wait while looking, believing, getting fooled, changing from day to day. Wait with the only kind of faith I have ever recognized, the faith that says I wanna know! I wanna see! I think I will understand when I do know and see. Meanwhile I'm not making any final judgments. Wait it out. Don't worry too much. You've got time. You're all right. You're reacting to life in the only way an intelligent, sensitive young man in a college can. In another year you'll enter another sphere of existence, the practical one. The knowledge, abstract now, which seems unrelated to sense to you (at times) will get a different color.

Sooner or later we all of us knock our heads against the ceiling of the world. It's like breaking a record: the last fifth of a second, which marks the difference between a good runner and a world beater is the hardest part of the whole proceeding. I mean that you, Bill, will be one of the minds of the world tomorrow. You will be the one, you and your generation, who will have to push knowledge of all sorts that inch ahead, which will make life tolerable in your day. Knowledge is limited, very limited, and it is only because you are in the preliminary stages of knowing that you think men, certain men, know so much more than you do. They may know a little more, but not the great amount that you imagine. For this reason, wait! Believe in yourself and your generation. Take it with a smile. That's what they mean when they speak of humor. It doesn't mean a guffaw or a grin. It means steadiness of nerves that is willing to bide its time, certain that with time a human adjustment can and will be made. It is the most that any man has ever been able to do.

Jumping to practical things: Have the Ford put in condition up there if you think the local mechanics can be trusted. Send me the bill. . . .

Mother and I both send love. Don't let *anything* get your goat and don't think you have to duck anything in life. There is a way out for every man who has the intellectual fortitude to go on in the face of difficulties.

Yours,
Dad

*   *

I can't help thinking there was something wrong about the advice you gave me.

W. SOMERSET MAUGHAM
The Facts of Life

It was Henry Garnet's habit on leaving the city of an afternoon to drop in at his club and play bridge before going home to dinner. He was a pleasant man to play with. He knew the game well and you could be sure that he would make the best of his cards. He was a good loser; and when he won was more inclined to ascribe his success to his luck than to his skill. He was indulgent, and if his partner made a mistake could be trusted to find an excuse for him. It was surprising then on this occasion to hear him telling his partner with unnecessary sharpness that he had never seen a hand worse played; and it was more surprising still to see him not only make a grave error himself, an error of which you would never have thought him capable, but when his partner, not unwilling to get a little of his own back, pointed it out, insist against all reason and with considerable heat that he was perfectly right. But they were all old friends, the men he was playing with, and none of them took his ill-humour very seriously. Henry Garnet was a broker, a partner in a firm of repute, and it occurred to one of them that something had gone wrong with some stock he was interested in.

"How's the market to-day?" he asked.

"Booming. Even the suckers are making money."

It was evident that stocks and shares had nothing to do with Henry Garnet's vexation; but something was the matter; that was evident too. He was a hearty fellow, who enjoyed excellent health; he had plenty of money; he was fond of his wife and devoted to his children. As a rule he had high spirits, and he laughed easily at the nonsense they were apt to talk while they played; but to-day he sat glum and silent. His brows were crossly puckered and there was a sulky look about his mouth. Presently, to ease the tension, one of the others mentioned a subject upon which they all knew Henry Garnet was glad to speak.

"How's your boy, Henry? I see he's done pretty well in the tournament."

Henry Garnet's frown grew darker.

"He's done no better than I expected him to."

"When does he come back from Monte?"

"He got back last night."

"Did he enjoy himself?"

"I suppose so; all I know is that he made a damned fool of himself."

"Oh. How?"

"I'd rather not talk about it if you don't mind."

The three men looked at him with curiosity. Henry Garnet scowled at the green baize.

"Sorry, old boy. Your call."

The game proceeded in a strained silence. Garnet got his bid, and when he played his cards so badly that he went three down not a word was said. Another rubber was begun and in the second game Garnet denied a suit.

"Having none?" his partner asked him.

Garnet's irritability was such that he did not even reply, and when at the end of the hand it appeared that he had revoked, and that his revoke cost the rubber, it was not to be expected that his partner should let his carelessness go without remark.

"What the devil's the matter with you, Henry?" he said. "You're playing like a fool."

Garnet was disconcerted. He did not so much mind losing a big rubber himself, but he was sore that his inattention should have made his partner lose too. He pulled himself together.

"I'd better not play any more. I thought a few rubbers would calm me, but the fact is I can't give my mind to the game. To tell you the truth I'm in a hell of a temper."

They all burst out laughing.

"You don't have to tell us that, old boy. It's obvious."

Garnet gave them a rueful smile.

"Well, I bet you'd be in a temper if what's happened to me had happened to you. As a matter of fact I'm in a damned awkward situation, and if any of you fellows can give me any advice how to deal with it I'd be grateful."

"Let's have a drink and you tell us all about it. With a K.C., a Home Office official and an eminent surgeon—if we can't tell you how to deal with a situation, nobody can."

The K.C. got up and rang the bell for a waiter.

"It's about that damned boy of mine," said Henry Garnet.

Drinks were ordered and brought. And this is the story that Henry Garnet told them.

The boy of whom he spoke was his only son. His name was Nicholas and of course he was called Nicky. He was eighteen. The Garnets had two daughters besides, one of sixteen and the other of twelve, but however unreasonable it seemed, for a father is generally supposed to like his daughters best, and though he did all he could not to show his preference, there was no doubt that the greater share of Henry Garnet's affection was given to his son. He was kind, in a chaffing, casual way, to his daughters, and gave them handsome presents on their birthdays and at Christmas; but he doted on Nicky. Nothing was too good for him. He thought the world of him. He could hardly take his eyes off him. You could not blame him, for Nicky was a son that any parent might have been proud of. He was six foot two, lithe but muscular, with broad shoulders and a slim waist, and he held himself gallantly erect; he had a charming head, well placed on the shoulders, with pale brown hair that waved slightly, blue eyes with long dark lashes under well-marked eyebrows, a full red mouth and a tanned, clean skin. When he smiled he showed very regular and very white teeth. He was not shy, but there was a modesty in his demeanour that was attractive. In social intercourse he was easy, polite and quietly gay. He was the offspring of nice, healthy, decent parents, he had been well brought up in a good home, he had been sent to a good school, and the general result was as engaging a specimen of young manhood as you were likely to find in a long time. You felt that he was as honest, open and virtuous as he looked. He had never given his parents a moment's uneasiness. As a child he was seldom ill and never naughty. As a boy he did everything that was expected of him. His school reports were excellent. He was wonderfully popular, and he ended his career, with a creditable number of prizes, as head of the school and captain of the football team. But this was not all. At the age of fourteen Nicky had developed an unexpected gift for lawn tennis. This was a game that his father not only was fond of, but played very well, and when he discerned in the boy the promise of a tennis-player he fostered it. During the holidays he had him taught by the best professionals and by the time he was sixteen he had won a number of tournaments for boys of his age. He could beat his father so badly that only parental affection reconciled the older player to the poor show he put up. At eighteen Nicky went to Cambridge and Henry Garnet conceived the ambition that before he was through with the university he should play for it. Nicky had all the qualifications for becoming a great tennis-player. He was tall, he had a long reach, he was quick on his feet and his timing was perfect. He realised instinctively where the ball was coming and, seemingly without hurry, was there to take it. He had a powerful serve, with a nasty break that made it difficult to return, and his forehand drive, low, long and accurate, was deadly. He was not so good on the backhand and his volleying was wild, but all through the summer before he went to Cambridge Henry Garnet made him work on these points under the best teacher in England. At the back of his mind, though he did not even mention it to Nicky, he cherished a further ambition, to see his son play at Wimbledon, and who could tell, perhaps be chosen to represent his country in the Davis Cup. A great lump came into Henry Garnet's throat as he saw in fancy his son leap over the net to shake hands with the American champion whom he had just defeated, and walk off the court to the deafening plaudits of the multitude.

As an assiduous frequenter of Wimbledon Henry Garnet had a good many friends in the tennis world, and one evening he found himself at a City dinner sitting next to one of them, a Colonel Brabazon, and in due course began talking to him of Nicky and what chance there might be of his being chosen to play for his university during the following season.

"Why don't you let him go down to Monte Carlo and play in the spring tournament there?" said the Colonel suddenly.

"Oh, I don't think he's good enough for that. He's not nineteen yet, he only went up to Cambridge last October; he wouldn't stand a chance against all those cracks."

"Of course, Austin and von Cramm and so on would knock spots off him, but he might snatch a game or two; and if he got up against some of the smaller fry there's no reason why he shouldn't win two or three matches. He's never been up against any of the first-rate players and it would be wonderful practice for him. He'd learn a lot more than he'll ever learn in the seaside tournaments you enter him for."

"I wouldn't dream of it. I'm not going to let him leave Cambridge in the middle of a term. I've always impressed upon him that tennis is only a game and it mustn't interfere with work."

Colonel Brabazon asked Garnet when the term ended.

"That's all right. He'd only have to cut about three days. Surely that could be arranged. You see, two of the men we were depending on have let us down, and we're in a hole. We want to send as good a team as we can. The Germans are sending their best players and so are the Americans."

"Nothing doing, old boy. In the first place Nicky's not good enough, and secondly, I don't fancy the idea of sending a kid like that to Monte Carlo without anyone to look after him. If I could get away myself I might think of it, but that's out of the question."

"I shall be there. I'm going as the non-playing captain of the English team. I'll keep an eye on him."

"You'll be busy, and besides, it's not a responsibility I'd like to ask you to take. He's never been abroad in his life, and to tell you the truth, I shouldn't have a moment's peace all the time he was there."

They left it at that and presently Henry Garnet went home. He was so flattered by Colonel Brabazon's suggestion that he could not help telling his wife.

"Fancy his thinking Nicky's as good as that. He told me he'd seen him play and his style was fine. He only wants more practice to get into the first flight. We shall see the kid playing in the semi-finals at Wimbledon yet, old girl."

To his surprise Mrs. Garnet was not so much opposed to the notion as he would have expected.

"After all the boy's eighteen. Nicky's never got into mischief yet and there's no reason to suppose he will now."

"There's his work to be considered; don't forget that. I think it would be a very bad precedent to let him cut the end of term."

"But what can three days matter? It seems a shame to rob him of a chance like that. I'm sure he'd jump at it if you asked him."

"Well, I'm not going to. I haven't sent him to Cambridge just to play tennis. I know he's steady, but it's silly to put temptation in his way. He's much too young to go to Monte Carlo by himself."

"You say he won't have a chance against these crack players, but you can't tell."

Henry Garnet sighed a little. On the way home in the car it had struck him that Austin's health was uncertain and that von Cramm had his off-days. Supposing, just for the sake of argument, that Nicky had a bit of luck like that—then there would be no doubt that he would be chosen to play for Cambridge. But of course that was all nonsense.

"Nothing doing, my dear. I've made up my mind and I'm not going to change it."

Mrs. Garnet held her peace. But next day she wrote to Nicky, telling him what had happened, and suggested to him what she would do in his place if, wanting to go, he wished to get his father's consent. A day or two later Henry Garnet received a letter from his son. He was bubbling over with excitement. He had seen his tutor, who was a tennis-player himself, and the Provost of his college, who happened to know Colonel Brabazon, and no objection would be made to his leaving before the end of term; they both thought it an opportunity that shouldn't be missed. He didn't see what harm he could come to, and if only, just this once, his father would stretch a point, well, next term, he promised faithfully, he'd work like blazes. It was a very pretty letter. Mrs. Garnet watched her husband read it at the breakfast table; she was undisturbed by the frown on his face. He threw it over to her.

"I don't know why you thought it necessary to tell Nicky something I told you in confidence. It's too bad of you. Now you've thoroughly unsettled him."

"I'm sorry. I thought it would please him to know that Colonel Brabazon had such a high opinion of him. I don't see why one should only tell people the disagreeable things that are said about them. Of course I made it quite clear that there could be no question of his going."

"You've put me in an odious position. If there's anything I hate it's for the boy to look upon me as a spoil-sport and a tyrant."

"Oh, he'll never do that. He may think you rather silly and unreasonable, but I'm sure he'll understand that it's only for his own good that you're being so unkind."

"Christ," said Henry Garnet.

His wife had a great inclination to laugh. She knew the battle was won. Dear, oh dear, how easy it was to get men to do what you wanted. For appearance sake Henry Garnet held out for forty-eight hours, but then he yielded, and a fortnight later Nicky came to London. He was to start for Monte Carlo next morning, and after dinner, when Mrs. Garnet and her elder daughter had left them, Henry took the opportunity to give his son some good advice.

"I don't feel quite comfortable about letting you go off to a place like Monte Carlo at your age practically by yourself," he finished, "but there it is and I can only hope you'll be sensible. I don't want to play the heavy father, but there are three things especially that I want to warn you against: one is gambling, don't gamble; the second is money, don't lend anyone money; and the third is women, don't have anything to do with women. If you don't do any of those three things you can't come to much harm, so remember them well."

"All right, father," Nicky smiled.

"That's my last word to you. I know the world pretty well and believe me, my advice is sound."

"I won't forget it. I promise you."

"That's a good chap. Now let's go up and join the ladies."

Nicky beat neither Austin nor von Cramm in the Monte Carlo tournament, but he did not disgrace himself. He snatched an unexpected victory over a Spanish player and gave one of the Austrians a closer match than anyone had thought possible. In the mixed doubles he got into the semi-finals. His charm conquered everyone and he vastly enjoyed himself. It was generally allowed that he showed promise, and Colonel Brabazon told him that when he was a little older and had had more practice with first-class players he would be a credit to his father. The tournament came to an end and the day following he was to fly back to London. Anxious to play his best he had lived very carefully, smoking little and drinking nothing, and going to bed early; but on his last evening he thought he would like to see something of the life in Monte Carlo of which he had heard so much. An official dinner was given to the tennis-players and after dinner with the rest of them he went into the Sporting Club. It was the first time he had been there. Monte Carlo was very full and the rooms were crowded. Nicky had never before seen roulette played except in the pictures; in a maze he stopped at the first table he came to; chips of different sizes were scattered over the green cloth in what looked like a hopeless muddle; the croupier gave the wheel a sharp turn and with a flick threw in the little white ball. After what seemed an endless time the ball stopped and another croupier with a broad, indifferent gesture raked in the chips of those who had lost.

Presently Nicky wandered over to where they were playing *trente et quarante*, but he couldn't understand what it was all about and he thought it dull. He saw a crowd in another room and sauntered in. A big game of baccara was in progress and he was immediately conscious of the tension. The players were protected from the thronging bystanders by a brass rail; they sat round the table, nine on each side, with the dealer in the middle and the croupier facing him. Big money was changing hands. The dealer was a member of the Greek Syndicate. Nicky looked at his impassive face. His eyes were watchful, but his expression never changed whether he won or lost. It was a terrifying, strangely impressive sight. It gave Nicky, who had been thriftily brought up, a peculiar thrill to see someone risk a thousand pounds on the turn of a card and when he lost make a little joke and laugh. It was all terribly exciting. An acquaintance came up to him.

"Been doing any good?" he asked.

"I haven't been playing."

"Wise of you. Rotten game. Come and have a drink."

"All right."

While they were having it Nicky told his friends that this was the first time he had ever been in the rooms.

"Oh, but you must have one little flutter before you go. It's idiotic to leave Monte without having tried your luck. After all it won't hurt you to lose a hundred francs or so."

"I don't suppose it will, but my father wasn't any too keen on my coming at all and one of the three things he particularly advised me not to do was to gamble."

But when Nicky left his companion he strolled back to one of the tables where they were playing roulette. He stood for a while looking at the losers' money being raked-in by the croupier and the money that was won paid out to the winners. It was impossible to deny that it was thrilling. His friend was right, it did seem silly to leave Monte without putting something on the table just once. It would be an experience, and at his age you had to have all the experience you could get. He reflected that he hadn't promised his father not to gamble, he'd promised him not to forget his advice. It wasn't quite the same, was it? He took a hundred-franc note out of his pocket and rather shyly put it on number eighteen. He chose it because that was his age. With a wildly beating heart he watched the wheel turn; the little white ball whizzed about like a small demon of mischief; the wheel went round more slowly, the little white ball hesitated, it seemed about to stop, it went on again; Nicky could hardly believe his eyes when it fell into number eighteen. A lot of chips were passed over to him and his hands trembled as he took them. It seemed to amount to a lot of money. He was so confused that he never thought of putting anything on the following round; in fact he had no intention of playing anymore, once was enough; and he was surprised when eighteen again came up. There was only one chip on it.

"By George, you've won again," said a man who was standing near to him.

"Me? I hadn't got anything on."

"Yes, you had. Your original stake. They always leave it on unless you ask for it back. Didn't you know?"

Another packet of chips was handed over to him. Nicky's head reeled. He counted his gains: seven thousand francs. A queer sense of power seized him; he felt wonderfully clever. This was the easiest way of making money that he had ever heard of. His frank, charming face was wreathed in smiles. His bright eyes met those of a woman standing by his side. She smiled.

"You're in luck," she said.

She spoke English, but with a foreign accent.

"I can hardly believe it. It's the first time I've ever played."

"That explains it. Lend me a thousand francs, will you? I've lost everything I've got. I'll give it you back in half an hour."

"All right."

She took a large red chip from his pile and with a word of thanks disappeared. The man who had spoken to him before grunted.

"You'll never see that again."

Nicky was dashed. His father had particularly advised him not to lend anyone money. What a silly thing to do! And to somebody he'd never seen in his life. But the fact was, he felt at that moment such a love for the human race that it had never occurred to him to refuse. And that big red chip, it was almost impossible to realise that it had any value. Oh well, it didn't matter, he still had six thousand francs, he'd just try his luck once or twice more and if he didn't win he'd go home. He put a chip on sixteen, which was his elder sister's age, but it didn't come up; then on twelve, which was his younger sister's, and that didn't come up either; he tried various numbers at random, but without success. It was funny, he seemed to have lost his knack. He thought he would try just once more and then stop; he won. He had made up all his losses and had something over. At the end of an hour, after various ups and downs, having experienced such thrills as he had never known in his life, he found himself with so many chips that they would hardly go in his pockets. He decided to go. He went to the changers' office and he gasped when twenty thousand-franc notes were spread out before him. He had never had so much money in his life. He put it in his pocket and was turning away when the woman to whom he had lent the thousand francs came up to him.

"I've been looking for you everywhere," she said. "I was afraid you'd gone. I was in a fever, I didn't know what you'd think of me. Here's your thousand francs and thank you so much for the loan."

Nicky, blushing scarlet, stared at her with amazement. How he had misjudged her! His father had said, don't gamble; well, he had, and he'd made twenty thousand francs; and his father had said, don't lend anyone money; well, he had, he'd lent quite a lot to a total stranger, and she'd returned it. The fact was that he wasn't nearly such a fool as his father thought; he'd had an instinct that he could lend her the money with safety, and you see, his instinct was right. But he was so obviously taken aback that the little lady was forced to laugh.

"What is the matter with you?" she asked.

"To tell you the truth I never expected to see the money back."

"What did you take me for? Did you think I was a—cocotte?"

Nicky reddened to the roots of his wavy hair.

"No, of course not."

"Do I look like one?"

"Not a bit."

She was dressed very quietly, in black, with a string of gold beads round her neck; her simple frock showed off a neat, slight figure; she had a pretty little face and a trim head. She was made up, but not excessively, and Nicky supposed that she was not more than three or four years older than himself. She gave him a friendly smile.

"My husband is in the administration in Morocco, and I've come to Monte Carlo for a few weeks because he thought I wanted a change."

"I was just going," said Nicky because he couldn't think of anything else to say.

"Already!"

"Well, I've got to get up early to-morrow. I'm going back to London by air."

"Of course. The tournament ended to-day, didn't it? I saw you play, you know, two or three times."

"Did you? I don't know why you should have noticed me."

"You've got a beautiful style. And you looked very sweet in your shorts."

Nicky was not an immodest youth, but it did cross his mind that perhaps she had borrowed that thousand francs in order to scrape acquaintance with him.

"Do you ever go to the Knickerbocker?" she asked.

"No. I never have."

"Oh, but you mustn't leave Monte Carlo without having been there. Why don't you come and dance a little? To tell you the truth, I'm starving with hunger and I should adore some bacon and eggs."

Nicky remembered his father's advice not to have anything to do with women, but this was different; you had only to look at the pretty little thing to know at once that she was perfectly respectable. Her husband was in what corresponded, he supposed, to the Civil Service. His father and mother had friends who

were Civil Servants and they and their wives sometimes came
to dinner. It was true that the wives were neither so young nor so
pretty as this one, but she was just as ladylike as they were. And
after winning twenty thousand francs he thought it wouldn't be
a bad idea to have a little fun.

"I'd love to go with you," he said. "But you won't mind if I
don't stay very long. I've left instructions at my hotel that I'm to
be called at seven."

"We'll leave as soon as ever you like."

Nicky found it very pleasant at the Knickerbocker. He ate his
bacon and eggs with appetite. They shared a bottle of champagne.
They danced, and the little lady told him he danced beautifully.
He knew he danced pretty well, and of course she was easy to
dance with. As light as a feather. She laid her cheek against his
and when their eyes met there was in hers a smile that made his
heart go pit-a-pat. A coloured woman sang in a throaty, sensual
voice. The floor was crowded.

"Have you ever been told that you're very good-looking?" she
asked.

"I don't think so," he laughed. "Gosh," he thought, "I believe
she's fallen for me."

Nicky was not such a fool as to be unaware that women often
liked him, and when she made that remark he pressed her to him
a little more closely. She closed her eyes and a faint sigh escaped
her lips.

"I suppose it wouldn't be quite nice if I kissed you before all
these people," he said.

"What do you think they would take me for?"

It began to grow late and Nicky said that really he thought he
ought to be going.

"I shall go too," she said. "Will you drop me at my hotel on
your way?"

Nicky paid the bill. He was rather surprised at its amount, but
with all that money he had in his pocket he could afford not to
care, and they got into a taxi. She snuggled up to him and he
kissed her. She seemed to like it.

"By Jove," he thought, "I wonder if there's anything doing."

It was true that she was a married woman, but her husband
was in Morocco, and it certainly did look as if she'd fallen for

him. Good and proper. It was true also that his father had warned
him to have nothing to do with women, but, he reflected again,
he hadn't actually promised he wouldn't, he'd only promised not
to forget his advice. Well, he hadn't; he was bearing it in mind
that very minute. But circumstances alter cases. She was a sweet
little thing; it seemed silly to miss the chance of an adventure
when it was handed to you like that on a tray. When they reached
the hotel he paid off the taxi.

"I'll walk home," he said. "The air will do me good after the
stuffy atmosphere of that place."

"Come up a moment," she said. "I'd like to show you the photo
of my little boy."

"Oh, have you got a little boy?" he exclaimed, a trifle dashed.

"Yes, a sweet little boy."

He walked upstairs after her. He didn't in the least want to see
the photograph of her little boy, but he thought it only civil to
pretend he did. He was afraid he'd made a fool of himself; it
occurred to him that she was taking him up to look at the photograph in order to show him in a nice way that he'd made a mistake. He'd told her he was eighteen.

"I suppose she thinks I'm just a kid."

He began to wish he hadn't spent all that money on champagne
at the night-club.

But she didn't show him the photograph of her little boy after
all. They had no sooner got into her room than she turned to
him, flung her arms round his neck, and kissed him full on the
lips. He had never in all his life been kissed so passionately.

"Darling," she said.

For a brief moment his father's advice once more crossed Nicky's
mind and then he forgot it.

Nicky was a light sleeper and the least sound was apt to wake
him. Two or three hours later he awoke and for a moment could
not imagine where he was. The room was not quite dark, for the
door of the bathroom was ajar, and the light in it had been left
on. Suddenly he was conscious that someone was moving about
the room. Then he remembered. He saw that it was his little
friend, and he was on the point of speaking when something in
the way she was behaving stopped him. She was walking very
cautiously, as though she were afraid of waking him; she stopped

once or twice and looked over at the bed. He wondered what she was after. He soon saw. She went over to the chair on which he had placed his clothes and once more looked in his direction. She waited for what seemed to him an interminable time. The silence was so intense that Nicky thought he could hear his own heart beating. Then, very slowly, very quietly, she took up his coat, slipped her hand into the inside pocket and drew out all those beautiful thousand-franc notes that Nicky had been so proud to win. She put the coat back and placed some other clothes on it so that it should look as though it had not been disturbed, then, with the bundle of notes in her hand, for an appreciable time stood once more stock-still. Nicky had repressed an instinctive impulse to jump up and grab her, it was partly surprise that had kept him quiet, partly the notion that he was in a strange hotel, in a foreign country, and if he made a row he didn't know what might happen. She looked at him. His eyes were partly closed and he was sure that she thought he was asleep. In the silence she could hardly fail to hear his regular breathing. When she had reassured herself that her movements had not disturbed him she stepped, with infinite caution, across the room. On a small table in the window a cineraria was growing in a pot. Nicky watched her now with his eyes wide open. The plant was evidently placed quite loosely in the pot, for taking it by the stalks she lifted it out; she put the banknotes in the bottom of the pot and replaced the plant. It was an excellent hiding-place. No one could have guessed that anything was concealed under that richly-flowering plant. She pressed the earth down with her fingers and then, very slowly, taking care not to make the smallest noise, crept across the room, and slipped back into bed.

"Chéri," she said, in a caressing voice.

Nicky breathed steadily, like a man immersed in deep sleep. The little lady turned over on her side and disposed herself to slumber. But though Nicky lay so still his thoughts worked busily. He was extremely indignant at the scene he had just witnessed, and to himself he spoke his thoughts with vigour.

"She's nothing but a damned tart. She and her dear little boy and her husband in Morocco. My eye! She's a rotten thief, that's what she is. Took me for a mug. If she thinks she's going to get away with anything like that, she's mistaken."

He had already made up his mind what he was going to do

with the money he had so cleverly won. He had long wanted a
car of his own, and had thought it rather mean of his father not
to have given him one. After all, a feller doesn't always want to
drive about in the family bus. Well, he'd just teach the old man
a lesson and buy one himself. For twenty thousand francs, two
hundred pounds roughly, he could get a very decent second-hand
car. He meant to get the money back, but just then he didn't
quite know how. He didn't like the idea of kicking up a row, he
was a stranger, in an hotel he knew nothing of; it might very well
be that the beastly woman had friends there, he didn't mind facing
anyone in a fair fight, but he'd look pretty foolish if someone
pulled a gun on him. He reflected besides, very sensibly, that he
had no proof the money was his. If it came to a showdown and
she swore it was hers, he might very easily find himself hauled off
to a police-station. He really didn't know what to do. Presently
by her regular breathing he knew that the little lady was asleep.
She must have fallen asleep with an easy mind, for she had done
her job without a hitch. It infuriated Nicky that she should rest
so peacefully while he lay awake worried to death. Suddenly an
idea occurred to him. It was such a good one that it was only by
the exercise of all his self-control that he prevented himself from
jumping out of bed and carrying it out at once. Two could play
at her game. She'd stolen his money; well, he'd steal it back again,
and they'd be all square. He made up his mind to wait quite
quietly until he was sure that deceitful woman was sound asleep.
He waited for what seemed to him a very long time. She did not
stir. Her breathing was as regular as a child's.

"Darling," he said at last.

No answer. No movement. She was dead to the world. Very
slowly, pausing after every movement, very silently, he slipped
out of bed. He stood still for a while, looking at her to see whether
he had disturbed her. Her breathing was as regular as before. During the time he was waiting he had taken note carefully of the
furniture in the room so that in crossing it he should not knock
against a chair or a table and make a noise. He took a couple of
steps and waited, he took a couple of steps more; he was very light
on his feet and made no sound as he walked; he took fully five
minutes to get to the window, and here he waited again. He
started, for the bed slightly creaked, but it was only because the

sleeper turned in her sleep. He forced himself to wait till he had counted one hundred. She was sleeping like a log. With infinite care he seized the cineraria by the stalks and gently pulled it out of the pot; he put his other hand in, his heart beat nineteen to the dozen as his fingers touched the notes, his hand closed on them and he slowly drew them out. He replaced the plant and in his turn carefully pressed down the earth. While he was doing all this he had kept one eye on the form lying in the bed. It remained still. After another pause he crept softly to the chair on which his clothes were lying. He first put the bundle of notes in his coat pocket and then proceeded to dress. It took him a good quarter of an hour, because he could afford to make no sound. He had been wearing a soft shirt with his dinner jacket, and he congratulated himself on this, because it was easier to put on silently than a stiff one. He had some difficulty in tying his tie without a looking-glass, but he very wisely reflected that it didn't really matter if it wasn't tied very well. His spirits were rising. The whole thing now began to seem rather a lark. At length he was completely dressed except for his shoes, which he took in his hand; he thought he would put them on when he got into the passage. Now he had to cross the room to get to the door. He reached it so quietly that he could not have disturbed the lightest sleeper. But the door had to be unlocked. He turned the key very slowly; it creaked.

"Who's that?"

The little woman suddenly sat up in bed. Nicky's heart jumped to his mouth. He made a great effort to keep his head.

"It's only me. It's six o'clock and I've got to go. I was trying not to wake you."

"Oh, I forgot."

She sank back on to the pillow.

"Now that you're awake I'll put on my shoes."

He sat down on the edge of the bed and did this.

"Don't make a noise when you go out. The hotel people don't like it. Oh, I'm so sleepy."

"You go right off to sleep again."

"Kiss me before you go." He bent down and kissed her. "You're a sweet boy and a wonderful lover. *Bon voyage.*"

Nicky did not feel quite safe till he got out of the hotel. The

dawn had broken. The sky was unclouded, and in the harbour the
yachts and the fishing-boats lay motionless on the still water. On
the quay fishermen were getting ready to start on their day's work.
The streets were deserted. Nicky took a long breath of the sweet
morning air. He felt alert and well. He also felt as pleased as
Punch. With a swinging stride, his shoulders well thrown back,
he walked up the hill and along the gardens in front of the Casino
—the flowers in that clear light had a dewy brilliance that was
delicious—till he came to his hotel. Here the day had already begun. In the hall porters with mufflers round their necks and berets
on their heads were busy sweeping. Nicky went up to his room and
had a hot bath. He lay in it and thought with satisfaction that
he was not such a mug as some people might think. After his bath
he did his exercises, dressed, packed and went down to breakfast.
He had a grand appetite. No continental breakfast for him! He
had grapefruit, porridge, bacon and eggs, rolls fresh from the oven,
so crisp and delicious they melted in your mouth, marmalade and
three cups of coffee. Though feeling perfectly well before, he felt
better after that. He lit the pipe he had recently learnt to smoke,
paid his bill and stepped into the car that was waiting to take
him to the aerodrome on the other side of Cannes. The road
as far as Nice ran over the hills and below him was the blue sea
and the coast-line. He couldn't help thinking it damned pretty.
They passed through Nice, so gay and friendly in the early morning, and presently they came to a long stretch of straight road
that ran by the sea. Nicky had paid his bill, not with the money
he had won the night before, but with the money his father had
given him; he had changed a thousand francs to pay for supper at
the Knickerbocker, but that deceitful little woman had returned
him the thousand francs he had lent her, so that he still had
twenty thousand-franc notes in his pocket. He thought he would
like to have a look at them. He had so nearly lost them that they
had a double value for him. He took them out of his hip-pocket
into which for safety's sake he had stuffed them when he put on
the suit he was travelling in, and counted them one by one. Something very strange had happened to them. Instead of there being
twenty notes as there should have been there were twenty-six.
He couldn't understand it at all. He counted them twice more.
There was no doubt about it; somehow or other he had twenty-six

thousand francs instead of the twenty he should have had. He couldn't make it out. He asked himself if it was possible that he had won more at the Sporting Club than he had realised. But no, that was out of the question; he distinctly remembered the man at the desk laying the notes out in four rows of five, and he had counted them himself. Suddenly the explanation occurred to him; when he had put his hand into the flower-pot, after taking out the cineraria, he had grabbed everything he felt there. The flower-pot was the little hussy's money-box and he had taken out not only his own money, but her savings as well. Nicky leant back in the car and burst into a roar of laughter. It was the funniest thing he had ever heard in his life. And when he thought of her going to the flower-pot some time later in the morning when she awoke, expecting to find the money she had so cleverly got away with, and finding, not only that it wasn't there, but that her own had gone too, he laughed more than ever. And so far as he was concerned there was nothing to do about it; he neither knew her name, nor the name of the hotel to which she had taken him. He couldn't return her money even if he wanted to.

"It serves her damned well right," he said.

This then was the story that Henry Garnet told his friends over the bridge-table, for the night before, after dinner when his wife and daughter had left them to their port, Nicky had narrated it in full.

"And you know what infuriated me is that he's so damned pleased with himself. Talk of a cat swallowing a canary. And d'you know what he said to me when he'd finished? He looked at me with those innocent eyes of his and said: 'You know, father, I can't help thinking there was something wrong about the advice you gave me. You said, don't gamble; well, I did, and I made a packet; you said, don't lend money; well, I did, and I got it back; and you said, don't have anything to do with women; well, I did, and I made six thousand francs on the deal.'"

It didn't make it any better for Henry Garnet that his three companions burst out laughing.

"It's all very well for you fellows to laugh, but you know, I'm in a damned awkward position. The boy looked up to me, he respected me, he took whatever I said as gospel truth, and now,

I saw it in his eyes, he just looks upon me as a drivelling old fool. It's no good my saying one swallow doesn't make a summer; he doesn't see that it was just a fluke, he thinks the whole thing was due to his own cleverness. It may ruin him."

"You do look a bit of a damned fool, old man," said one of the others. "There's no denying that, is there?"

"I know I do, and I don't like it. It's so dashed unfair. Fate has no right to play one tricks like that. After all, you must admit that my advice was good."

"Very good."

"And the wretched boy ought to have burnt his fingers. Well, he hasn't. You're all men of the world, you tell me how I'm to deal with the situation now."

But they none of them could.

"Well, Henry, if I were you I wouldn't worry," said the lawyer. "My belief is that your boy's born lucky, and in the long run that's better than to be born clever or rich."

*   *

. . . go by ways less treacherous than these.

LEE HATFIELD
To Telemachus

If you must leave these shores, my son,
Go by other ways than we have gone,
That your ribs be not broken
On the shingled strand of Circe's island—
That on the Siren's reef your blood
Shall not be mingled with the ancient corpses.

For between the whirlpool and the rock
The channel is a narrow one, and not without its
Fickle tides and doldrums; and we who
Once sailed too near the Scylla wonder often
In the night, in the calm between two dreams,
Whether we survived or perished there.

And so if you must leave these shores
Listen first to those warnings that the seas
Whisper hoarsely in the night,
And go by ways less treacherous than these.

For by whatever course you travel
You will learn that the way leads always
Back to Ithaca.
                        And once returned, it is only
By a difference in the pattern of our wounds
That you will know
                        Yourself
                                From myself.

. . . TO A DAUGHTER

Be very good.

RICHARD HARDING DAVIS

from

A LETTER TO HIS DAUGHTER HOPE*

October 24

MY DEAR DAUGHTER:

So many weeks have passed since I saw you that by now you are able to read this without your mother looking over your shoulder and helping you with the big words. I have six sets of pictures of you. Every day I take them down and change them. Those your dear mother put in glass frames I do not change. Also, I have all the sweet

---

* The famous war correspondent Richard Harding Davis sent his daughter this advice in 1915 when she was nine months old and he was fifty-one and en route to Europe.

fruits and chocolates and red bananas. How good of you to think of just the things your father likes. . . .

Be very good. Do not bump yourself. Do not eat matches. Do not play with scissors or cats. Do not forget your dad. Sleep when your mother wishes it. Love us both. Try to know how we love you. *That* you will never learn. Good-night and God keep you, and bless you.

Your Dad

*   *

Stand up and act like a big girl.

BUDD SCHULBERG

A Short Digest of a Long Novel

HER LEGS were shapely and firm and when she crossed them and smiled with the self-assurance that always delighted him, he thought she was the only person he knew in the world who was unblemished. Not lifelike but an improvement on life, as a work of art, her delicate features were chiseled from a solid block. The wood-sculpture image came easy to him because her particular shade of blonde always suggested maple polished to a golden grain. As it had been from the moment he stood in awe and amazement in front of the glass window where she was first exhibited, the sight of her made him philosophical. Some of us appear in beautiful colors, too, or with beautiful grains, but we develop imperfections. Inspect us very closely and you find we're damaged by the elements. Sometimes we're only nicked with cynicism. Sometimes we're cracked with disillusionment. Or we're split with fear.

When she began to speak, he leaned forward, eager for the words that were like good music, profundity expressed in terms that pleased the ear while challenging the mind.

"Everybody likes me," she said. "Absolutely everybody."

It was not that she was conceited. It was simply that she was only three. No one had ever taken her with sweet and whispered promises that turned into morning-after lies, ugly and cold as unwashed dishes from last night's dinner lying in the sink. She had never heard a dictator rock her country to sleep with peaceful lullabies one day and rock it with bombs the next. She was unde-ceived. Her father ran his hands reverently through her soft yel-low hair. She is virgin, he thought, for this is the true virginity, that brief moment in the time of your life before your mind or your body has been defiled by acts of treachery.

It was just before Christmas and she was sitting on her little chair, her lips pressed together in concentration, writing a last-minute letter to Santa Claus. The words were written in some language of her own invention but she obligingly translated as she went along.

Dear Santa, I am a very good girl and everybody likes me. So please don't forget to bring me a set of dishes, a doll that goes to sleep and wakes up again, and a washing machine. I need the washing machine because Raggedy Ann's dress is so dirty.

After she had finished her letter, folded it, and asked him to address it, he tossed her up in the air, caught her and tossed her again, to hear her giggle. "Higher, Daddy, higher," she instructed. His mind embraced her sentimentally: She is a virgin island in a lewd world. She is a winged seed of innocence blown through the wasteland. If only she could root somewhere. If only she could grow like this.

"Let me down, Daddy," she said when she decided that she had indulged him long enough, "I have to mail my letter to Santa."

"But didn't you see him this afternoon?" he asked. "Didn't you ask for everything you wanted? Mommy said she took you up to meet him and you sat on his lap."

"I just wanted to remind him," she said. "There were so many other children."

He fought down the impulse to laugh, because she was not something to laugh at. And he was obsessed with the idea that to hurt her feelings with laughter was to nick her, to blemish the perfection.

"Daddy can't catch me-ee," she sang out, and the old chase

was on, following the pattern that had become so familiar to them, the same wild shrieks and the same scream of pretended anguish at the inevitable result. Two laps around the dining-room table was the established course before he caught her in the kitchen. He swung her up from the floor and set her down on the kitchen table. She stood on the edge, poised confidently for another of their games. But this was no panting, giggling game like tag or hide-and-seek. This game was ceremonial. The table was several feet higher than she was. "Jump, jump, and Daddy will catch you," he would challenge. They would count together, *one, two* and on *three* she would leap out into the air. He would not even hold out his arms to her until the last possible moment. But he would always catch her. They had played the game for more than a year and the experience never failed to exhilarate them. You see, I am always here to catch you when you are falling, it said to them, and each time she jumped, her confidence increased and their bond deepened.

They were going through the ceremony when the woman next door came in with her five-year-old son, Billy. "Hello, Mr. Steevers," she said. "Would you mind if I left Bill with you for an hour while I go do my marketing?"

"No, of course not, glad to have him," he said and he mussed Billy's hair playfully. "How's the boy, Billy?"

But his heart wasn't in it. This was his only afternoon of the week with her and he resented the intrusion. And then too, he was convinced that Billy was going to grow up into the type of man for whom he had a particular resentment. A sturdy, good-looking boy, big for his age, aggressively unchildlike, a malicious, arrogant, insensitive extrovert. I can just see him drunk and red-faced and pulling up girls' dresses at Legion Conventions, Mr. Steevers would think. And the worst of it was, his daughter seemed blind to Billy's faults. The moment she saw him she forgot about their game.

"Hello, Billy-Boy," she called and ran over to hug him.

"I want a cookie," said Billy.

"Oh, yes, a cookie; some animal crackers, Daddy."

She had her hostess face on and as he went into the pantry, he could hear the treble of her musical laughter against the premature baritone of Billy's guffaws.

He swung open the pantry door with the animal crackers in his hand just in time to see it. She was poised on the edge of the table. Billy was standing below her, as he had seen her father do. "Jump and I'll catch you," he was saying.

Smiling, confident and unblemished, she jumped. But no hands reached out to break her flight. With a cynical grin on his face, Billy stepped back and watched her fall.

Watching from the doorway, her father felt the horror that possessed him the time he saw a parachutist smashed like a bug on a windshield when his chute failed to open. She was lying there, crying, not so much in pain as in disillusionment. He ran forward to pick her up and he would never forget the expression on her face, the *new* expression, unchildlike, unvirginal, embittered.

"I hate you, I hate you," she was screaming at Billy through hysterical sobs.

Well, now she knows, thought her father, the facts of life. Now she's one of us. Now she knows treachery and fear. Now she must learn to replace innocence with courage.

She was still bawling. He knew these tears were as natural and as necessary as those she shed at birth, but that could not overcome entirely the heavy sadness that enveloped him. Finally, when he spoke, he said, a little more harshly than he had intended, "Now, now, stop crying. Stand up and act like a big girl. A little fall like that can't hurt you."

*   *

From 8 to 10, practice music.

THOMAS JEFFERSON
A Letter to His Daughter Martha*

Annapolis, Nov. 28th, 1783

My Dear Patsy—After four days' journey, I arrived here without any accident, and in as good health as when I left Philadelphia. The

---

* Martha Jefferson was eleven when her father wrote her this letter from Annapolis, Maryland, where he was attending meetings of the Federal Congress. Her mother had recently died.

conviction that you would be more improved in the situation I have placed you than if still with me, has solaced me on my parting with you, which my love for you has rendered a difficult thing. The acquirements which I hope you will make under the tutors I have provided for you will render you more worthy of my love; and if they cannot increase it, they will prevent its diminution. Consider the good lady who has taken you under her roof, who has undertaken to see that you perform all your exercises, and to admonish you in all those wanderings from what is right or what is clever, to which your inexperience would expose you: consider her, I say, as your mother, as the only person to whom, since the loss with which Heaven has pleased to afflict you, you can now look up; and that her displeasure or disapprobation, on any occasion, will be an immense misfortune, which should you be so unhappy as to incur by any unguarded act, think no concession too much to regain her good-will. With respect to the distribution of your time, the following is what I should approve:

From 8 to 10, practice music.
From 10 to 1, dance one day and draw another.
From 1 to 2, draw on the day you dance, and write a letter next day.
From 3 to 4, read French.
From 4 to 5, exercise yourself in music.
From 5 till bed-time, read English, write, etc.

Communicate this plan to Mrs. Hopkinson, and if she approves it, pursue it. As long as Mrs. Trist remains in Philadelphia, cultivate her affection. She has been a valuable friend to you, and her good sense and good heart make her valued by all who know her, and by nobody on earth more than me. I expect you will write me by every post. Inform me what books you read, what tunes you learn, and enclose me your best copy of every lesson in drawing. Write also one letter a week either to your Aunt Eppes, your Aunt Skipwith, your Aunt Carr, or the little lady from whom I now enclose a letter, and always put the letter you so write under cover to me. Take care that you never spell a word wrong. Always before you write a word, consider how it is spelt, and, if you do not remember it, turn to a dictionary. It produces great praise to a lady to spell well. I have placed my happiness on seeing you good and accomplished; and no distress which this world can now bring on me would equal that of your disappointing my hopes. If you love me, then strive to be good under every situation and to all living creatures, and to acquire those accomplishments which I have put in your power, and which will go far towards ensuring you the warmest love of your affectionate father,

Th. Jefferson

P.S.—Keep my letters and read them at times, that you may always have present in your mind those things which will endear you to me.

*   *

Don't worry about the past. Don't worry about the future.

F. SCOTT FITZGERALD

A LETTER TO HIS DAUGHTER SCOTTY*

La Paix, Rodgers' Forge
Towson, Maryland
August 8, 1933

DEAR PIE:

I feel very strongly about you doing [your] duty. Would you give me a little more documentation about your reading in French? I am glad you are happy—but I never believe much in happiness. I never believe in misery either. Those are things you see on the stage or the screen or the printed page, they never really happen to you in life.

All I believe in in life is the rewards for virtue (according to your talents) and the *punishments* for not fulfilling your duties, which are doubly costly. If there is such a volume in the camp library, will you ask Mrs. Tyson to let you look up a sonnet of Shakespeare's in which the line occurs *"Lilies that fester smell far worse than weeds."*

Have had no thoughts today, life seems composed of getting up a *Saturday Evening Post* story. I think of you, and always pleasantly; but if you call me "Pappy" again I am going to take the White Cat out and beat his bottom *hard, six times for every time you are impertinent.* Do you react to that?

I will arrange the camp bill.

Halfwit, I will conclude.

Things to worry about:
   Worry about courage
   Worry about cleanliness
   Worry about efficiency
   Worry about horsemanship
   Worry about . . .
Things not to worry about:
   Don't worry about popular opinion
   Don't worry about dolls
   Don't worry about the past
   Don't worry about the future

---

* Frances Scott Fitzgerald was not quite twelve and was away at camp when this stern list of admonitions arrived from a father anxious that she avoid his failings and mistakes.

Don't worry about growing up
Don't worry about anybody getting ahead of you
Don't worry about triumph
Don't worry about failure unless it comes through your own fault
Don't worry about mosquitoes
Don't worry about flies
Don't worry about insects in general
Don't worry about parents
Don't worry about boys
Don't worry about disappointments
Don't worry about pleasures
Don't worry about satisfactions
Things to think about:
What am I really aiming at?
How good am I really in comparison to my contemporaries in regard
to:
(a) Scholarship?
(b) Do I really understand about people and am I able to get along
with them?
(c) Am I trying to make my body a useful instrument or am I
neglecting it?

> With dearest love,
> [Daddy]

P.S. My come-back to your calling me Pappy is christening you by
the word Egg, which implies that you belong to a very rudimentary
state of life and that I could break you up and crack you open at my
will and I think it would be a word that would hang on if I ever told
it to your contemporaries. "Egg Fitzgerald." How would you like that
to go through life with—"Eggie Fitzgerald" or "Bad Egg Fitzgerald"
or any form that might occur to fertile minds? Try it once more and
I swear to God I will hang it on you and it will be up to you to shake
it off. Why borrow trouble?

> Love anyhow.

*   *

The main point is to avoid affectation. . . .

WILLIAM FREND

from

A LETTER TO HIS DAUGHTER SOPHIA*

. . . I MAY ADD that I not only do not object, but approve of it, as you go in a party in whom I can place the utmost confidence. It is rather too soon for you to go to such places, which are neither to be eagerly sought after, nor to be fastidiously rejected. Though I was early initiated into the mysteries of dancing, and by a residence in France, before I went to College, acquired a somewhat greater skill in capering than the generality of young men of my age, yet I did not go to a ball, except in vacation times in the country, till I had taken my first degree. Young as you are, yet I can trust you in a ball-room without any fears of your being guilty of impropriety; yet there are a few things worth your knowing, and some against which you should be on your guard. The main point is to avoid affectation of every kind, whether in walk, gesture, or talk. In the common modes of dancing you have had instruction enough, and of them I say nothing. Anything like romping in dancing is to be carefully avoided. There is a certain distance to be moved over in a given time. I have seen girls scurrying through twice that distance, and thinking they had done a great feat; but, in fact, they only made themselves ridiculous, and looked like hoydens. Mind your time and the figure of the dance, and should you ever in the latter be set right by your neighbour, take it in good part, and be sure you make him or her sensible you feel obliged to them. I perceive by your letter that you already have two partners, but should you have any other, which I don't object to, don't stand like a statue, but converse with him freely, if he is so inclined; but beware of making any remark that is to the disadvantage of any person in the room. Use your eyes well; look about you and notice those who appear to be the most graceful in their gestures and manner of conversation. You may probably have some people of rank there, ladies who discredit by their rude, dashing behaviour, and others who do credit to their station by propriety of conduct. There is an awkward bashfulness and a bold look of self-importance, between which is the happy medium which distinguishes a well-bred woman. Few are there that

---

* William Frend was an English actuary early in the nineteenth century. When he wrote this letter to his daughter giving her permission to attend her first ball, she was sixteen and he was approaching sixty-nine.

can make either a good bow or a good curtsey. I care not whether it
is a low one, as in my time, or a nod, or a slip, as is now the fashion;
there is grace in doing either, which, if you cannot attain, still the
extreme may be avoided. Observe what is done by others, but avoid
imitation; what may be graceful in one may not suit another. Each
has a suitable modification peculiar to himself which, if it is changed
by affectation, makes him ridiculous. The great secret, however, is to
carry with you a cheerful and innocent heart, desirous of giving and
receiving all the satisfaction which the amusement is capable of afford-
ing, wishing no ill to your neighbours, passing over their faults, and
highly regarding their excellences. Though the eyes of many may be
upon you, yet you are to act as if no one regarded you, careful only
that what you are about you do as well as you can. I shall be glad to
hear your remarks on the first exhibition of the kind that you have
been at.

*   *

Keep on having your gay time, but just keep yourself in hand. . . .

OGDEN NASH

A Letter to His Daughter Isabel

Dearest Isabel,

I gather that by now you have decided Mr. X is too old for you,
as well as being a very silly man, but I am not pleased by the episode
and I trust that by now you aren't either. The propensity of old men
for flirting with young girls has been the object of coarse merriment
since primeval days, as I should think your reading, if nothing else,
should have told you.

You should be intelligent enough to know that in various eras of
history it has been fashionable to laugh at morals, but the fact of the
matter is that Old Man Morals just keeps rolling along and the
laughers end up as driftwood on a sandbar. You can't beat the game,
because morals as we know them represent the sum of the experience
of the race. That is why it distressed me to find you glibly tossing off
references to divorce. You surely have seen enough of its effects on
your friends to know that it is a tragic thing even when forced on one
partner by the vices of the other.

Read the marriage vows again—they are not just words, not even just a poetic promise to God. They are a practical promise to yourself to be happy. This I know from simply looking around me.

It bothers me to think that you may have sloppy—not sophisticated but sloppy—ideas about life. I have never tried to blind you to any side of life, through any form of censorship, trusting in your intelligence to learn of, and to recognize, evil without approving or participating in it. So please throw Iris March and all the golden doomed Bohemian girls away and be Isabel—there's more fun in it for you.

Keep on having your gay time, but just keep yourself in hand, and remember that generally speaking it's better to call older men Mister.

I love you tremendously,
Daddy

DISCIPLINARIAN

He that spareth his rod hateth his son; but he that loveth him chasteneth him betimes.

PROVERBS XIII:24

Many a father spanks his child for things his father should have spanked out of him.

DON MARQUIS

My father was very loving but very severe; his severity made him the more endearing. In my relations with him I was like the people who live at the foot of a volcano. . . . Each morning and evening is displayed a new and charming aspect of the mountain, but all at once it will send up huge columns of fire and emit voluminous heavy stones from its quiet cone, the sight of which can never be erased from one's memory.

KAZUO KOIZUMI: from FATHER AND I

*　　　*

Now tell me everything . . . just the way it happened.

MARK SCHORER
WHAT WE DON'T KNOW HURTS US

THE MID-AFTERNOON WINTER SUN burned through the high California haze. Charles Dudley, working with a mattock in a thicket of overgrowth, felt as steamy and as moldy as the black adobe earth in which his feet kept slipping. Rain had fallen for five days with no glimmer of sunshine, and now it seemed as if the earth, with fetid animation, like heavy breath, were giving all that moisture back to the air. The soil, or the broom which he was struggling to uproot, had a disgusting, acrid odor, as if he were tussling with some obscene animal instead of with a lot of neglected vegetation, and suddenly an overload of irritations—the smell, the stinging sweat in his eyes, his itching skin, his blistering palms—made him throw the mattock down and come diving out of the thicket into the clearing he had already achieved.

'Is it hard?'

He looked up and saw Josephine, his wife, sitting on the railing of the balcony onto which the French doors of their bedroom

85

opened. She was holding a dust mop, and a tea towel was wrapped around her head, and her face seemed pallid and without character, as it always did to Charles when she neglected to wear lipstick.

He snorted instead of replying, and wiped his muddy hands on the seat of his stiff new levis. Then he walked over to the short flight of steps that led up to the balcony from the garden, and lit a cigarette.

'It looks as though the ground levels out up there where you're working,' Josephine said.

'Yes, it does. Somebody once had a terrace up there. It's full of overgrown geraniums that are more like snakes, and a lot of damned rose vines.'

'You've got the pepper tree almost free. It's going to be very nice, isn't it?'

He looked up at the pepper tree, with its delicate, drooping branches and the long gray tendrils that hung down from the branches to the ground. He had chopped out the broom as far up the incline as the tree, and now he could see that a big branch of the eucalyptus at the very edge of the property had forced the top of the pepper tree to grow out almost horizontally from the main portion of its trunk. 'Look at the damned thing!' he said.

'It's charming, like a Japanese print.'

'I'm going to hate this house long before it's livable,' he said.

'Oh, Charles!'

'I didn't want to buy a house. I never wanted to own any house. I certainly never wanted to own a miserable, half-ruined imitation of a Swiss chalet built on an incline that was meant for goats.' Vehemently he flipped his cigarette up into the pile of brush he had accumulated.

Josephine stood up and shook out the dust mop. 'Let's not go into all that again. There was no choice. It's no pleasure for me, either, living the way we are, nor is it for the children.' She paused, and then she added a cold supplement. 'I sometimes think that your disinclination to own anything is a form of irresponsibility.' She turned swiftly and went into the house.

He stood staring after her, frowning a little, for it seemed momentarily that with studied intent she had cracked the bland habit of her amiability. But in a minute she reappeared in the doorway and said matter-of-factly, 'I heard on the radio that Boston has had eighteen inches of snow.' Then she went back inside.

'Are you trying to make me homesick?' he asked of no one as he started back up the incline, and he remembered the frozen river, snow blowing over the Esplanade, and city lights faint in a blizzard.

He began again to chop at the roots of the broom. All right, he told himself, so he was being unpleasant. He did not like the idea of being pinned down by a mortgage to a place his firm had picked for him. He did not even like the idea of being pinned down by a mortgage. To own something was, to that extent, to be owned, and he did not like the feeling. His idea of a good way to live was in a duplex apartment owned by someone else, in Charles River Square, or, better than that but always less likely, in a duplex apartment owned by someone else, on the East River. He connected happiness with a certain luxury, and, probably, sexuality with elegance and freedom. These were not noble associations, he was aware, and he knew that it was foolish to let impossibilities, as they faded, become forms of minor torture. This knowledge made him chop more angrily than ever at the broom.

It was vegetation with which Charles felt that he had a peculiar intimacy, perhaps the only thing in California which, in the several weeks they had lived there, he had really come to know. And he loathed it with a violence which he recognized as quite undue, and which, now, made him feel childish and curiously guilty. Yet he could not laugh away his loathing. The stuff was ubiquitous, and sprang up anywhere at all the minute the ground was neglected. If it grew up in a patch, it began a foolish competition with itself, and the thin, naked stalks shot ten and twelve and fourteen feet into the air, all stretching up to the sun for the sake of a plume of paltry foliage at the top. Then the foliage tangled together in a thatch, and when you had managed to chop out the shallow roots of the tree, you still had to extricate its trivial but tenacious branches from those of all its neighbors to get it out of the clump. Once it was out, the wood was good for nothing, but dried up into a kind of bamboo stalk so insubstantial that it did not make even decent kindling. As a tree it was a total fraud, and in spite of the nuisance of its numbers, and of its feminine

air of lofty self-importance, it was, with its shallow roots in this
loose soil, very vulnerable to attack. Charles beat away at it in
an angry frenzy, as if he were overwhelming, after a long struggle,
some bitter foe.

He did not hear his son come up the incline behind him, and
the boy stood quietly watching until his father turned to toss a
stalk up on the pile in the clearing. Then the boy said, 'Hi.' He
said it tentatively, almost shyly, as though his father's responses
were unpredictable.

'Hi, Gordon.'

'What're you doing?'

'Can't you see? How was school?'

'It stinks,' he answered doggedly, his dark eyes half-averted and
sorrowful.

Charles felt a twinge of pain for him. 'Cheer up. Give it time.
You'll get to like it after a while.'

'I'll never like it,' Gordon said stubbornly.

Charles took up his mattock again. 'Sure you will,' he said as
he began to swing it.

'Nobody likes me.'

Charles let the mattock come to rest and, turning once more
to the boy, he spoke with an impatient excess of patience. 'You
say that every day. I've told you it isn't true. You're a new boy in
the school, and you came in the middle of the term, and there's
never yet been a new boy who entered a school late and made
friends right away. You're nearly nine, and you can understand
that. Anyway, I'm tired of explaining it to you.'

'When can I get a paper route?'

Charles laughed without humor. 'My God, boy! Give us a
chance to get settled.'

'I need money.'

'You get an allowance.'

'I need more money,' the boy insisted. 'I want a paper route.
How do kids get them?'

'You can work for me. You can get in there with a hedge
shears and cut out all those vines.'

The boy looked at his father despairingly and shook his head.
'No, I need a lot of money.'

'You can earn a lot of money working for me,' Charles said,
swinging his mattock.

'I need a dollar,' Gordon said faintly.

His father did not hear him, and he did not turn from his work again until presently he heard his daughter calling him shrilly from the foot of the hill on which the house stood.

'What is it?' he called back. She was climbing the path, and he saw that she had a white envelope in her hand.

Then Gordon broke into rapid, desperate speech. 'I need a dollar. I'll pay it back out of my allowance. Remember yesterday I told you about that dollar I found? I have to pay it back.'

Charles stared at him. 'What dollar?'

Gordon glanced wildly over his shoulder. His sister, holding the menacing white envelope in one hand and her workman's tin lunchbox in the other, was halfway up the hill, coming along the side of the house. Pleadingly, Gordon looked back at his father. 'The dollar. Remember? I told you I found it. You wanted to know what I did with it.'

'What dollar?'

He sighed. 'You didn't listen! You never listen!'

Charles patted his shoulder. 'Now take it easy. Don't get excited. Tell me again. I don't think you told me anything about a dollar yesterday.'

'The dollar I found. You asked me what I did with it, and I told you I gave it to Crow, and you said I should have brought it home to you.'

'That Crow! I thought you were joking.'

Penelope, the six-year-old, was behind him now, and Gordon's shoulders sagged in despair. 'I wasn't joking,' he said almost wearily as Penelope handed his father the letter. 'You never really listen.'

Charles read the precise handwriting on the envelope. 'Mr. or Mrs. Dudley,' it said, and in the lower left-hand corner, 'Courtesy of Penelope.' He opened the envelope and read the message:

Dear Mr. and Mrs. Dudley—
Gordon became involved in some difficulty about a dollar today, and I wish you would help me. The dollar was lunch money belonging to a girl who says she left it deep in her coat pocket, in the cloak room, yesterday. When I brought it up with Gordon, he immediately said that he did not steal it. He says that he found it on the floor, and he also says that he told his father about it yesterday and that his father said he should have brought it home to him, and now he is fixed in his confusions. He gave it to an older boy named Will Crow, who spent it, and I have told Gordon that he will have to return a

dollar to the girl tomorrow. Gordon is a very worthwhile little personality, but I do not think he has been entirely happy here at the Crestview School, and therefore, if you can help me straighten this out to his own best interest, I will be ever so grateful.

Sincerely yours,
Gertrude Grandjent,
Principal.

Charles groaned in exasperation. 'My God, why did you have to drag me into it? What will that woman think?'

Gordon's lips were trembling. 'You remember? I did tell you, didn't I?'

'Yes, I remember now. I remember very clearly that you told me you found it on the way to school, and when I asked you what you did with it, and you said you gave it to Crow, naturally I said you should have brought it home. *Listen*, Gordon—' The very simplicity of the boy's strategy infuriated Charles, and it was with an effort that he controlled his temper. He said, 'Penny, you go in now and tell your mother you're home.'

Penny was staring at her brother. 'What did Gordon do?'

'Run along, Penny, as I told you.'

She went down the incline reluctantly, staring back over her shoulder, and when she had gone into the house, Charles turned to Gordon again and said, 'Sit down.'

They sat down side by side on the damp slope. Gordon said, 'Will you lend me a dollar and keep my allowance until it's made up? I have to take it back tomorrow.'

'We'll talk about that later.' Charles tapped the letter with his muddy hand. 'Why did you tell me you found it in the street?'

Gordon looked away but answered promptly. 'I knew if I told you I found it in school, you'd have said I should have taken it to the office.'

'So you lied to me instead. That was better?'

Gordon did not answer.

'Answer me.'

'Yes.'

'Yes, what?'

'I lied.'

That was that. Charles started over. 'Why did you tell Miss Grandjent that you did not steal it when she hadn't even said you had?'

'I knew that's what she thought.'

'How did you know?'

'I just knew.'

Charles hesitated. When he spoke again, his voice was warmer, friendly, almost confidential. 'What's the little girl's name, Gordon?'

'She's not little. She's in high fourth.'

'What's her name?'

'I don't know. Joan, I guess.'

'What color is her coat?'

Gordon glanced at his father sharply. 'I don't know. I never noticed it.'

Charles bit his lip in exasperation and stood up. 'Let's go inside.' He led the way in.

Josephine was standing on a chair in the middle of the living room. She was dusting the hideous chandelier of dark metal and colored glass which hung from the center of the ceiling. It was only one of many distasteful features in the house which the Dudleys hoped to rid it of, but it was hard to find men to do all the necessary work, and none would promise to do it quickly. An electrician had torn away a good deal of plaster and lathing, and a carpenter had ripped out some bookshelves and ugly mantels and taken down most of a wall between the dining room and a useless hallway, but neither had returned, and painters, plasterers, paper hangers had not yet come at all. The Dudleys had decided to leave most of their belongings in storage until the work was done, and to bring nothing out of storage that they cared about. The result was that the house was almost fantastically disordered and bleak and squalid, and while Josephine managed to keep an even temper under these conditions, Charles, who found them very trying, did not.

He stood in the doorway of the living room now and said to her, 'Why do you bother?'

'The light was so dim,' she said, and then, seeing his expression, asked quickly, 'What's wrong?'

'Another problem.' He came heavily into the living room and gave her the letter. She read it standing on the chair, her face expressionless. Then she stepped down and went out into the hall where Gordon was lurking and said, 'Come in, dear.'

There was one old sofa in the room, and Josephine sat down

there with Gordon. Charles sat facing them on the single straight chair. Josephine took Gordon's hands and said, 'Now tell me everything, Gordon, just the way it happened.'

The boy's face was composed in a kind of stolid determination, but when he raised his moody eyes from the bare floor to his father, his chin began to tremble, his eyelids fluttered, and suddenly the dogged expression broke in despair, his body sagged, his head fell back against the sofa, and he burst into harsh sobs. Josephine put her arm around his shoulders and held him close while he cried, and she shook her head sharply at Charles as he jumped up impatiently. He sat down again. Finally Gordon stopped crying, almost as abruptly as he had begun.

'How did it happen, Gordon?' his mother asked.

He straightened up and stared at the floor again. 'Nothing happened. I just came in the cloak room and saw it on the floor. I took it and put it in my pocket, and at recess I gave it to Crow.'

'Didn't anyone see you pick it up?'

'There wasn't anyone else there.'

'In the cloak room? Before school? Why not?'

'I was late.'

'Late? But why? You left here in plenty of time.'

'I stopped on the way and played with a cat.'

Josephine frowned. 'So there was no one else there at all to see you?' she asked meaningfully.

'No.'

Josephine glanced at Charles. He drew his lips apart and, with a heavy satiric edge, said, 'Well, Gordon, that's too bad! If there'd been someone else there, you could prove that you hadn't—'

Josephine broke in. 'Tell me just where the dollar was, Gordon,' she said softly, and her voice had no relation to the look in her eyes as she glared at Charles.

'On the floor.'

'But exactly where? Was it near the little girl's coat?'

'She isn't little.'

'Was it near her coat?'

'I don't know which coat is hers.'

'Was it near any coat?'

'It was on the floor, near all of them. They hang on a rack, and it was on the floor near them.'

Josephine paused, and Gordon wriggled his shoulders out from under her arm and slumped in the corner of the sofa, away from her. 'When can I get out of here?' he asked.

'When you start answering our questions,' his father said sharply. 'You insist that you didn't steal it?'

Gordon raised his lids slowly, as if they were very heavy, and stared out at his father from under his brows. 'I found it on the floor.'

Josephine spoke brightly. 'Very well. We have settled that. But Gordon, surely you don't think that because you found it on the floor, it belonged to you? Don't you see that it was just as much stealing it as if you had really taken it from the pocket of the person it belonged to?'

'Not as much,' Gordon said.

'But it wasn't *yours!* You knew that.'

The boy nodded.

'Well, then—

'Someone else would have found it!'

'But would someone else have kept it?'

'I didn't keep it.'

Charles leaped up from his chair. 'That's the point! Why in God's name did you give it to that Crow rat?'

'He's my friend,' Gordon said with simple defiance, and then he slid off the sofa and lay on the floor.

'Your friend! A fine friend!' Charles shouted in disgust, standing over him. 'Get up!'

Gordon did not make any effort to move, and Josephine grasped Charles's arm. 'Let me,' she said quietly. 'Sit down.'

'Nonsense!' he cried angrily at her, and pulled his arm free of her touch. 'I'll take over now.' He seized the boy by the shoulders and pulled him up on the sofa. The jerk which he gave his body made the boy's head bob back and forward like a doll's, and he slumped against the sofa back almost as if he had been injured, dull eyes staring out of his pale face. 'Now listen to me, Gordon. I don't know if you took that money out of someone's pocket or not, but it looks, from the way you're behaving, as if you did. Anyway, you took it. It didn't belong to you, you knew that, and yet you took it. Do you see that there is no difference between the floor and the pocket as long as you kept it?'

' I didn't keep it,' Gordon repeated, but almost listlessly.

'Oh, my God!' Charles ran his hand through his hair, and the rumpled hair gave him a sudden wild look. 'Listen,' he said as quietly as he could, 'we are all having a very hard time here. We are trying to live in a house that isn't fit to live in. I am trying to get used to a new office. Your mother—'

Josephine said, 'Don't bother about me.'

'I will bother! We are all having a tough time, and Gordon can't think of anything better to do than to get into this mess at school. Of all the friends you could pick, you pick that nasty Crow brat, who is too old for you by three years and is a snide little—'

'Charles!'

Gordon lay back on the sofa. He looked ill and defeated.

'Will you admit that you stole that dollar? That taking it from the floor was just as much stealing it as if you had taken it from the pocket?'

'Yes,' he answered faintly.

'Speak up!'

'Yes, I *do!*' Gordon cried, and turned his face away.

Then the room was very still. Josephine stood stiffly beside the couch, her eyes fixed on Charles with dismay. Charles sagged a little, as if he, too, were defeated. And Gordon might have been asleep or dreaming, so remote had he suddenly become. Then they all heard a sly noise at the door, and Charles and Josephine swung toward it. Penelope stood there, embarrassed to have been caught. She giggled and said, 'Why did Gordon steal money?'

'Go away,' Charles said.

'Go to your room, dear,' Josephine said, 'or go outside.'

'But why did Gordon steal money?'

Charles walked to the girl, gave her a little push, and closed the door on her face. Then he came back to the sofa. He sat down next to Gordon, and when he spoke, his voice was nearly lifeless. 'You want to earn that dollar. All right, you can, Gordon. First go to your room and write your five sentences. Do them quickly for a change, and then go out into that patch of broom with the hedge shears and cut down all the vines you can find in it. You have an hour left before it gets dark.'

Gordon's eyes dreamed over his father's face, and then he slowly got up and left the room. His parents watched him go, and when he had closed the door softly behind him, Charles broke out. 'What is it, what stubbornness, that makes that boy so impenetrable? Did he steal that money or not? I haven't the slightest idea. All I could do was force him to admit that there was no difference between the two things.'

Josephine was looking at him with studied appraisal.

'Well?' he challenged her.

'You forced his admission. Did that gain anything? And what did it lose? How much did it hurt him? Is it of very great importance whether he stole it or not?'

'I don't know what's more important.'

'No, I really think you don't.'

'Well?'

'What's more important is why he took it, and what he did with it, and why he did that. What's more important is that he's a miserable little boy, and that you haven't made the slightest effort to understand *that*. All you've done is played the heavy parent, shown him that you don't trust him or believe him, and left him with a nice new layer of solidified guilt, and what is he supposed to do with *that*?'

'Let's skip the psychology for a change,' Charles said. 'There is an old-fashioned principle of honesty and dishonesty.'

'There's a more old-fashioned one of simple perception!' Josephine's face was red with anger. She stood in the middle of the bare room and looked rapidly around her, as if she felt a sudden desperate need, a hunger, for objects. But there was only the sofa, the chair, and Charles. Her eyes came back to him.

'Have you thought of his difficulties at all? Just the simple matter of his writing, for example? He came from a school where the children printed, and he printed as well as anyone. He comes here where the children do cursive writing, and of course he's made to feel like a fool, and he has to practice at home to learn it when other boys are playing. Or have you once helped him with that? Have you even suggested a sentence he might write? No. All you've done is to give him the extremely comforting bit of information that new boys, especially if they enter school late, have a hard time making friends! The one friend he has made you deride. No, don't interrupt. I know he's a horrid boy. I don't want Gordon playing with him either. But you haven't the sense to see that what has brought them together is that they are both pariahs. I think Gordon's giving that dollar to that dreadful boy is one of the most touching things I've ever heard of!'

'If what you've told me about Crow is true,' Charles said quietly, 'I won't have Gordon playing with him, and that's that.'

'Because Crow taught him some nasty words and told him some nasty, mistaken things about sex! You're perfectly right. But you can't just stand there and say no to him! If you were half a father, you would have told him yourself. *You* should be his friend! You're the one who should be giving him a decent attitude toward those things. You *are* his father, after all.'

'Oh, listen— He's not even nine!'

'All right. But he's getting it, isn't he? And all wrong?' And then, without warning, she sat down heavily on the single chair and began to sob, her reddened face lifted, her mouth twisted in sorrow, tears streaming down over her cheeks. 'All *wrong!*' she wailed.

Charles went to her quickly and, half standing, half kneeling beside the chair, awkwardly put his arms around her. 'Josephine, listen—'

'Oh, I know!' she sobbed. 'We all get in your way. We're all a nuisance that you're saddled with! We all just *bother* you! I know! It just isn't your idea of the way to live. You really hate it, don't you?'

His arms tightened. 'Darling,' he said, 'don't be a damned fool. Listen, I love you, I love the kids. Why, little Penny, I—'

'Oh, yes. Penny, sure! She's tractable! She doesn't raise any problems. That's different!'

'You're crazy. Gordon, too. You. Maybe I'm not much good with him, but that doesn't mean . . . And listen . . . I'll try. I'll go out there now.'

She dug in her pocket for a piece of Kleenex. She blew her nose and wiped her eyes. She pulled the tea towel off her head and shook out her hair. Then she blew her nose again. 'I'm all right now,' she said, getting up. She picked up the dust cloth which she had flung over the back of the chair, and she said, 'It's probably just this awful house, the way we have to camp. I'm going to get cleaned up and dress, and I'm going to find a table cloth, and we'll have dinner at a table tonight, instead of sitting on the floor with plates in our laps.'

He said, 'Good girl! I'll go and fix it up with Gordon.'

Charles went into Gordon's room. It was empty. He glanced at the table where Gordon worked and saw that there was a sheet of writing there. Then he looked out of the window and saw the boy on his hands and knees in among the remaining broom. He crossed the hall to the bedroom where Josephine was dressing. 'I may not be very subtle with him, but I seem to get results,' he said. She merely glanced up at him, and as he went out on the balcony, down the steps, and up the slippery incline, he felt no satisfaction whatever in his remark.

'How's it going?' he asked the boy.

Gordon glanced over his shoulder. 'All right,' he said, and turned at once to his job. The hedge shears made a busy, innocent sound.

Charles found his mattock where he had dropped it, and began to chop at the edge of the overgrowth again. Immediately his nostrils filled with the poisonous smell he had noticed before, his hands began to chafe, and even though the heat of the sun had gone in the late afternoon, sweat broke out with a prickling sensation all over his face and body. Once more he was tense with irritation, and he said, 'That awful smell! What is it?'

'I don't know,' Gordon replied without looking up.

'Like something decaying.'

The boy did not answer, and Charles chopped angrily away at a root. When it came free, he shook the earth off and tossed the slim tree down the slope. 'This crazy, piddling stuff!' he shouted, and then reminded himself that it was only a kind of exaggerated weed, a thing that grew everywhere, so futile that it could not even send down a decent root and was hardly designed as a personal affront to him. Or was it? He laughed and started to chop at the next root, but stopped at once. 'I'm quitting for today,' he said. 'Come on, let's go in.'

Gordon said, 'No, I'll work a while. I want to earn the money.'

'Oh, let it go. We'll fix that up.'

Gordon stared at him. 'I want to earn it,' he said, and went on clipping at the rose vines.

'All right,' Charles said, 'but come in soon. You'll have to wash up thoroughly to get that muck off.'

He went back into the house by way of the bedroom, but Josephine was no longer there. He went into Gordon's room, but she was not there, either. On the table lay the white sheet of ruled paper covered with the boy's writing, his five sentences in their hasty, uncertain, and very large cursive characters. Charles picked it up. The first sentence was, 'I am going to cut vins.' The second was, 'I am going to ern mony.' The third was, 'The sun is shining.' The fourth was, 'When it rains here it rains hard.' The last, which seemed to have been written with greater care, with a kind of precision and flourish which his writing had never shown before, was, 'You hate me and I hate you.'

Charles took a sharp breath and held it, then sagged. After a moment he walked to the window and put his forehead against the cool glass. He stared out into the desolate garden, at the bare earth and the darkening tangle, and tried to think. When he heard Josephine moving on high heels somewhere in the rugless house, he began to fold the sheet of paper, and he folded it again and again, until it was a small hard square. This he stuffed deep into his pocket.

He came into the hall and saw Josephine standing in the center of the barren living room. She looked tall in an old but still handsome black housecoat, a straight, severe garment which hung from the tightly belted waist in heavy folds, and was without ornament or color anywhere. Her hair was pulled tautly away from her face, and her face was smooth and white, and her mouth was painted dark red.

She was detached from the room, from the house, and utterly from him—remote and beautiful, cold in resolution. Never in the ten years he had known her had she appeared so wonderfully in possession of herself. And, helplessly, Charles turned away.

He went into the boy's room again, and looked out to see the boy. But twilight had obscured the garden now, shadows hung about it like veils, and Charles could hardly see into the trees. Then he thought that he saw Gordon's shape, hunched on the ground among the slim trunks, and he went out quickly to find him. Perhaps, even now, after everything, it was the boy who, somehow, could help.

. . . The climax had come over the Saturday movie. Kate, who had been pushed a little too far herself, said he couldn't go to the movie until he straightened up his room.

"I thought housework was a woman's job," Goggle had said.

I sent him up to his room with a good whack on the behind to hasten his progress, and when he got there he slammed the door so hard that the house shook.

I ran upstairs after him, seeing red. . . .

BENTZ PLAGEMANN: from FATHER TO THE MAN

*   *

My father's bark was always more to be feared than his bite. He would threaten loudly, but punish mildly or not at all.

JOHN BURROUGHS

ENEMY

Lizzie Borden took an ax
And gave her mother 40 whacks;
When she saw what she had done,
She gave her father 41.

UNKNOWN

*Mummy . . . if I prayed hard would God send Daddy
back to the war?*

FRANK O'CONNOR
My Oedipus Complex

FATHER WAS IN THE ARMY all through the war—the first war, I
mean—so, up to the age of five, I never saw much of him, and
what I saw did not worry me. Sometimes I woke and there was a
big figure in khaki peering down at me in the candlelight. Sometimes in the early morning I heard the slamming of the front
door and the clatter of nailed boots down the cobbles of the lane.
These were Father's entrances and exits. Like Santa Claus he came
and went mysteriously.

In fact, I rather liked his visits, though it was an uncomfortable
squeeze between Mother and him when I got into the big bed in
the early morning. He smoked, which gave him a pleasant musty
smell, and shaved, an operation of astounding interest. Each time
he left a trail of souvenirs—model tanks and Gurkha knives with
handles made of bullet cases, and German helmets and cap badges
and button-sticks, and all sorts of military equipment—carefully
stowed away in a long box on top of the wardrobe, in case they
ever came in handy. There was a bit of the magpie about Father;
he expected everything to come in handy. When his back was
turned, Mother let me get a chair and rummage through his treas-
ures. She didn't seem to think so highly of them as he did.

The war was the most peaceful period of my life. The window
of my attic faced southeast. My mother had curtained it, but that
had small effect. I always woke with the first light and, with all
the responsibilities of the previous day melted, feeling myself
rather like the sun, ready to illumine and rejoice. Life never seemed
so simple and clear and full of possibilities as then. I put my feet
out from under the clothes—I called them Mrs. Left and Mrs.
Right—and invented dramatic situations for them in which they

discussed the problems of the day. At least Mrs. Right did; she
was very demonstrative, but I hadn't the same control of Mrs. Left,
so she mostly contented herself with nodding agreement.

They discussed what Mother and I should do during the day,
what Santa Claus should give a fellow for Christmas, and what
steps should be taken to brighten the home. There was that little
matter of the baby, for instance. Mother and I could never agree
about that. Ours was the only house in the terrace without a new
baby, and Mother said we couldn't afford one till Father came
back from the war because they cost seventeen and six. That
showed how simple she was. The Geneys up the road had a baby,
and everyone knew they couldn't afford seventeen and six. It was
probably a cheap baby, and Mother wanted something really good,
but I felt she was too exclusive. The Geneys' baby would have
done us fine.

Having settled my plans for the day, I got up, put a chair under
the attic window, and lifted the frame high enough to stick out my
head. The window overlooked the front gardens of the terrace
behind ours, and beyond these it looked over a deep valley to the
tall, red-brick houses terraced up the opposite hillside, which were
all still in shadow, while those at our side of the valley were all
lit up, though with long strange shadows that made them seem
unfamiliar; rigid and painted.

After that I went into Mother's room and climbed into the big
bed. She woke and I began to tell her of my schemes. By this time,
though I never seem to have noticed it, I was petrified in my night-
shirt, and I thawed as I talked until, the last frost melted, I fell
asleep beside her and woke again only when I heard her below in
the kitchen, making the breakfast.

After breakfast we went into town; heard Mass at St. Augustine's
and said a prayer for Father, and did the shopping. If the afternoon
was fine we either went for a walk in the country or a visit to
Mother's great friend in the convent, Mother St. Dominic. Mother
had them all praying for Father, and every night, going to bed, I
asked God to send him back safe from the war to us. Little, indeed,
did I know what I was praying for!

One morning, I got into the big bed, and there, sure enough,
was Father in his usual Santa Claus manner, but later, instead of
uniform, he put on his best blue suit, and Mother was as pleased

as anything. I saw nothing to be pleased about, because, out of uniform, Father was altogether less interesting, but she only beamed,
and explained that our prayers had been answered, and off we
went to Mass to thank God for having brought Father safely home.

The irony of it! That very day when he came in to dinner he took
off his boots and put on his slippers, donned the dirty old cap he
wore about the house to save him from colds, crossed his legs, and
began to talk gravely to Mother, who looked anxious. Naturally,
I disliked her looking anxious, because it destroyed her good looks,
so I interrupted him.

"Just a moment, Larry!" she said gently.

This was only what she said when we had boring visitors, so I
attached no importance to it and went on talking.

"Do be quiet, Larry!" she said impatiently. "Don't you hear me
talking to Daddy?"

This was the first time I had heard those ominous words, "talking to Daddy," and I couldn't help feeling that if this was how
God answered prayers, he couldn't listen to them very attentively.

"Why are you talking to Daddy?" I asked with as great a show
of indifference as I could muster.

"Because Daddy and I have business to discuss. Now, don't interrupt again!"

In the afternoon, at Mother's request, Father took me for a
walk. This time we went into town instead of out the country, and
I thought at first, in my usual optimistic way, that it might be an
improvement. It was nothing of the sort. Father and I had quite
different notions of a walk in town. He had no proper interest in
trams, ships, and horses, and the only thing that seemed to divert
him was talking to fellows as old as himself. When I wanted to
stop he simply went on, dragging me behind him by the hand;
when he wanted to stop I had no alternative but to do the same.
I noticed that it seemed to be a sign that he wanted to stop for
a long time whenever he leaned against a wall. The second time
I saw him do it I got wild. He seemed to be settling himself forever. I pulled him by the coat and trousers, but, unlike Mother
who, if you were too persistent, got into a wax and said: "Larry,
if you don't behave yourself, I'll give you a good slap," Father
had an extraordinary capacity for amiable inattention. I sized him
up and wondered would I cry, but he seemed to be too remote to

be annoyed even by that. Really, it was like going for a walk with a mountain! He either ignored the wrenching and pummeling entirely, or else glanced down with a grin of amusement from his peak. I had never met anyone so absorbed in himself as he seemed.

At teatime, "talking to Daddy" began again, complicated this time by the fact that he had an evening paper, and every few minutes he put it down and told Mother something new out of it. I felt this was foul play. Man for man, I was prepared to compete with him any time for Mother's attention, but when he had it all made up for him by other people it left me no chance. Several times I tried to change the subject without success.

"You must be quiet while Daddy is reading, Larry," Mother said impatiently.

It was clear that she either genuinely liked talking to Father better than talking to me, or else that he had some terrible hold on her which made her afraid to admit the truth.

"Mummy," I said that night when she was tucking me up, "do you think if I prayed hard God would send Daddy back to the war?"

She seemed to think about that for a moment.

"No, dear," she said with a smile. "I don't think he would."

"Why wouldn't he, Mummy?"

"Because there isn't a war any longer, dear."

"But, Mummy, couldn't God make another war, if He liked?"

"He wouldn't like to, dear. It's not God who makes wars, but bad people."

"Oh!" I said.

I was disappointed about that. I began to think that God wasn't quite what he was cracked up to be.

Next morning I woke at my usual hour, feeling like a bottle of champagne. I put out my feet and invented a long conversation in which Mrs. Right talked of the trouble she had with her own father till she put him in the Home. I didn't quite know what the Home was but it sounded the right place for Father. Then I got my chair and stuck my head out of the attic window. Dawn was just breaking, with a guilty air that made me feel I had caught it in the act. My head bursting with stories and schemes, I stumbled in next door, and in the half-darkness scrambled into the big bed.

There was no room at Mother's side so I had to get between her and Father. For the time being I had forgotten about him, and for several minutes I sat bolt upright, racking my brains to know what I could do with him. He was taking up more than his fair share of the bed, and I couldn't get comfortable, so I gave him several kicks that made him grunt and stretch. He made room all right, though. Mother waked and felt for me. I settled back comfortably in the warmth of the bed with my thumb in my mouth.

"Mummy!" I hummed, loudly and contentedly.

"Sssh! dear," she whispered. "Don't wake Daddy!"

This was a new development, which threatened to be even more serious than "talking to Daddy." Life without my early-morning conferences was unthinkable.

"Why?" I asked severely.

"Because poor Daddy is tired."

This seemed to me a quite inadequate reason, and I was sickened by the sentimentality of her "poor Daddy." I never liked that sort of gush; it always struck me as insincere.

"Oh!" I said lightly. Then in my most winning tone: "Do you know where I want to go with you today, Mummy?"

"No, dear," she sighed.

"I want to go down the Glen and fish for thornybacks with my new net, and then I want to go out to the Fox and Hounds, and—"

"Don't-wake-Daddy!" she hissed angrily, clapping her hand across my mouth.

But it was too late. He was awake, or nearly so. He grunted and reached for the matches. Then he stared incredulously at his watch.

"Like a cup of tea, dear?" asked Mother in a meek, hushed voice I had never heard her use before. It sounded almost as though she were afraid.

"Tea?" he exclaimed indignantly. "Do you know what the time is?"

"And after that I want to go up the Rathcooney Road," I said loudly, afraid I'd forget something in all those interruptions.

"Go to sleep at once, Larry!" she said sharply.

I began to snivel. I couldn't concentrate, the way that pair went

on, and smothering my early-morning schemes was like burying
a family from the cradle.

Father said nothing, but lit his pipe and sucked it, looking out
into the shadows without minding Mother or me. I knew he was
mad. Every time I made a remark Mother hushed me irritably.
I was mortified. I felt it wasn't fair; there was even something
sinister in it. Every time I had pointed out to her the waste of
making two beds when we could both sleep in one, she had told
me it was healthier like that, and now here was this man, this
stranger, sleeping with her without the least regard for her health!

He got up early and made tea, but though he brought Mother
a cup he brought none for me.

"Mummy," I shouted, "I want a cup of tea, too."

"Yes, dear," she said patiently. "You can drink from Mummy's
saucer."

That settled it. Either Father or I would have to leave the
house. I didn't want to drink from Mother's saucer; I wanted to
be treated as an equal in my own home, so, just to spite her, I
drank it all and left none for her. She took that quietly, too.

But that night when she was putting me to bed she said gently:

"Larry, I want you to promise me something."

"What is it?" I asked.

"Not to come in and disturb poor Daddy in the morning.
Promise?"

"Poor Daddy" again! I was becoming suspicious of everything
involving that quite impossible man.

"Why?" I asked.

"Because poor Daddy is worried and tired and he doesn't sleep
well."

"Why doesn't he, Mummy?"

"Well, you know, don't you, that while he was at the war
Mummy got the pennies from the Post Office?"

"From Miss MacCarthy?"

"That's right. But now, you see, Miss MacCarthy hasn't any
more pennies, so Daddy must go out and find us some. You know
what would happen if he couldn't?"

"No," I said, "tell us."

"Well, I think we might have to go out and beg for them like the poor old woman on Fridays. We wouldn't like that, would we?"

"No," I agreed. "We wouldn't."

"So you'll promise not to come in and wake him?"

"Promise."

Mind you, I meant that. I knew pennies were a serious matter, and I was all against having to go out and beg like the old woman on Fridays. Mother laid out all my toys in a complete ring round the bed so that, whatever way I got out, I was bound to fall over one of them.

When I woke I remembered my promise all right. I got up and sat on the floor and played—for hours, it seemed to me. Then I got my chair and looked out the attic window for more hours. I wished it was time for Father to wake; I wished someone would make me a cup of tea. I didn't feel in the least like the sun; instead, I was bored and so very, very cold! I simply longed for the warmth and depth of the big featherbed.

At last I could stand it no longer. I went into the next room. As there was still no room at Mother's side I climbed over her and she woke with a start.

"Larry," she whispered, gripping my arm very tightly," what did you promise?"

"But I did, Mummy," I wailed, caught in the very act. "I was quiet for ever so long."

"Oh, dear, and you're perished!" she said sadly, feeling me all over. "Now, if I let you stay will you promise not to talk?"

"But I want to talk, Mummy," I wailed.

"That has nothing to do with it," she said with a firmness that was new to me. "Daddy wants to sleep. Now, do you understand that?"

I understood it only too well. I wanted to talk, he wanted to sleep—whose house was it, anyway?

"Mummy," I said with equal firmness, "I think it would be healthier for Daddy to sleep in his own bed."

That seemed to stagger her, because she said nothing for a while.

"Now, once for all," she went on, "you're to be perfectly quiet or go back to your own bed. Which is it to be?"

The injustice of it got me down. I had convicted her out of her own mouth of inconsistency and unreasonableness and she hadn't even attempted to reply. Full of spite, I gave Father a kick, which she didn't notice but which made him grunt and open his eyes in alarm.

"What time is it?" he asked in a panic-stricken voice, not looking at Mother but at the door, as if he saw someone there.

"It's early yet," she replied soothingly. "It's only the child. Go to sleep again. . . . Now, Larry," she added, getting out of bed, "you've wakened Daddy and you must go back."

This time, for all her quiet air, I knew she meant it, and knew that my principal rights and privileges were as good as lost unless I asserted them at once. As she lifted me, I gave a screech, enough to wake the dead, not to mind Father. He groaned.

"That damn child! Doesn't he ever sleep?"

"It's only a habit, dear," she said quietly, though I could see she was vexed.

"Well, it's time he got out of it," shouted Father, beginning to heave in the bed. He suddenly gathered all the bedclothes about him, turned to the wall, and then looked back over his shoulder with nothing showing only two small, spiteful, dark eyes. The man looked very wicked.

To open the bedroom door, Mother had to let me down, and I broke free and dashed for the farthest corner, screeching. Father sat bolt up right in bed.

"Shut up, you little puppy!" he said in a choking voice.

I was so astonished that I stopped screeching. Never, never had anyone spoken to me in that tone before. I looked at him incredulously and saw his face convulsed with rage. It was only then that I fully realized how God had codded me, listening to my prayers for the safe return of this monster.

"Shut up, you!" I bawled, beside myself.

"What's that you said?" shouted Father, making a wild leap out of the bed.

"Mick, Mick!" cried Mother. "Don't you see the child isn't used to you?"

"I see he's better fed than taught," snarled Father, waving his arms wildly. "He wants his bottom smacked."

All his previous shouting was as nothing to these obscene words referring to my person. They really made my blood boil.

"Smack your own!" I screamed hysterically. "Smack your own! Shut up! Shut up!"

At this he lost his patience and let fly at me. He did it with the lack of conviction you'd expect of a man under Mother's horrified eyes, and it ended up as a mere tap, but the sheer indignity of being struck at all by a stranger, a total stranger who had cajoled his way back from the war into our big bed as a result of my innocent intercession, made me completely dotty. I shrieked and shrieked, and danced in my bare feet, and Father, looking awkward and hairy in nothing but a short grey army shirt, glared down at me like a mountain out for murder. I think it must have been then that I realized he was jealous too. And there stood Mother in her nightdress, looking as if her heart was broken between us. I hoped she felt as she looked. It seemed to me that she deserved it all.

From that morning out my life was a hell. Father and I were enemies, open and avowed. We conducted a series of skirmishes against one another, he trying to steal my time with Mother and I his. When she was sitting on my bed, telling me a story, he took to looking for some pair of old boots which he alleged he had left behind him at the beginning of the war. While he talked to Mother I played loudly with my toys to show my total lack of concern. He created a terrible scene one evening when he came in from work and found me at his box, playing with his regimental badges, Gurkha knives and button-sticks. Mother got up and took the box from me.

"You mustn't play with Daddy's toys unless he lets you, Larry," she said severely. "Daddy doesn't play with yours."

For some reason Father looked at her as if she had struck him and then turned away with a scowl.

"Those are not toys," he growled, taking down the box again to see had I lifted anything. "Some of those curios are very rare and valuable."

But as time went on I saw more and more how he managed to alienate Mother and me. What made it worse was that I couldn't grasp his method or see what attraction he had for Mother. In every possible way he was less winning than I. He had a common accent and made noises at his tea. I thought for a while that it might be the newspapers she was interested in, so I made up bits of news of my own to read to her. Then I thought it might be the smoking, which I personally thought attractive, and took his pipes and went round the house dribbling into them till he caught me. I even made noises at my tea, but Mother only told me I was disgusting. It all seemed to hinge round that unhealthy habit of sleeping together, so I made a point of dropping into their bedroom and nosing round, talking to myself, so that they wouldn't know I was watching them, but they were never up to anything that I could see. In the end it beat me. It seemed to depend on being grown-up and giving people rings, and I realized I'd have to wait.

But at the same time I wanted him to see that I was only waiting, not giving up the fight. One evening when he was being particularly obnoxious, chattering away well above my head, I let him have it.

"Mummy," I said, "do you know what I'm going to do when I grow up?"

"No, dear," she replied. "What?"

"I'm going to marry you," I said quietly.

Father gave a great guffaw out of him, but he didn't take me in. I knew it must only be pretence. And Mother, in spite of everything, was pleased. I felt she was probably relieved to know that one day Father's hold on her would be broken.

"Won't that be nice?" she said with a smile.

"It'll be very nice," I said confidently. "Because we're going to have lots and lots of babies."

"That's right, dear," she said placidly. "I think we'll have one soon, and then you'll have plenty of company."

I was no end pleased about that because it showed that in spite of the way she gave in to Father she still considered my wishes. Besides, it would put the Geneys in their place.

It didn't turn out like that, though. To begin with, she was very preoccupied—I supposed about where she would get the seventeen and six— and though Father took to staying out late in the evenings it did me no particular good. She stopped taking me for walks, became as touchy as blazes, and smacked me for

nothing at all. Sometimes I wished I'd never mentioned the con-
founded baby—I seemed to have a genius for bringing calamity
on myself.

And calamity it was! Sonny arrived in the most appalling hulla-
baloo—even that much he couldn't do without a fuss—and from
the first moment I disliked him. He was a difficult child—so far
as I was concerned he was always difficult—and demanded far too
much attention. Mother was simply silly about him, and couldn't
see when he was only showing off. As company he was worse than
useless. He slept all day, and I had to go round the house on tiptoe
to avoid waking him. It wasn't any longer a question of not waking Father. The slogan now was "Don't-wake-Sonny!" I couldn't
understand why the child wouldn't sleep at the proper time, so
whenever Mother's back was turned I woke him. Sometimes to
keep him awake I pinched him as well. Mother caught me at it
one day and gave me a most unmerciful flaking.

One evening, when Father was coming in from work, I was playing trains in the front garden. I let on not to notice him; instead,
I pretended to be talking to myself, and said in a loud voice: "If
another bloody baby comes into this house, I'm going out."

Father stopped dead and looked at me over his shoulder.

"What's that you said?" he asked sternly.

"I was only talking to myself," I replied, trying to conceal my
panic. "It's private."

He turned and went in without a word. Mind you, I intended
it as a solemn warning, but its effect was quite different. Father
started being quite nice to me. I could understand that, of course.
Mother was quite sickening about Sonny. Even at mealtimes she'd
get up and gawk at him in the cradle with an idiotic smile, and
tell Father to do the same. He was always polite about it, but he
looked so puzzled you could see he didn't know what she was
talking about. He complained of the way Sonny cried at night,
but she only got cross and said that Sonny never cried except when
there was something up with him—which was a flaming lie, because Sonny never had anything up with him, and only cried for
attention. It was really painful to see how simple-minded she was.
Father wasn't attractive, but he had a fine intelligence. He saw
through Sonny, and now he knew that I saw through him as well.

One night I woke with a start. There was someone beside me

in the bed. For one wild moment I felt sure it must be Mother, having come to her senses and left Father for good, but then I heard Sonny in convulsions in the next room, and Mother saying: "There! There! There!" and I knew it wasn't she. It was Father. He was lying beside me, wide awake, breathing hard and apparently as mad as hell.

After a while it came to me what he was mad about. It was his turn now. After turning me out of the big bed, he had been turned out himself. Mother had no consideration now for anyone but that poisonous pup, Sonny. I couldn't help feeling sorry for Father. I had been through it all myself, and even at that age I was magnanimous. I began to stroke him down and say: "There! There!" He wasn't exactly responsive.

"Aren't you asleep either?" he snarled.

"Ah, come and put your arm around us, can't you?" I said, and he did, in a sort of way. Gingerly, I suppose, is how you'd describe it. He was very bony but better than nothing.

At Christmas he went out of his way to buy me a really nice model railway.

*   *

Father and son are natural enemies and each is happier and more secure in keeping it that way.

JOHN STEINBECK: from
CONVERSATION AT SAG HARBOR

*   *

You think you're better'n your father, now, don't you . . . ?

SAMUEL CLEMENS

from

THE ADVENTURES OF HUCKLEBERRY FINN: "PAP STARTS IN ON A NEW LIFE"

I HAD SHUT THE DOOR TO. Then I turned around, and there he was. I used to be scared of him all the time, he tanned me so much. I reckoned I was scared now, too; but in a minute I see I was mistaken—that is, after the first jolt, as you may say, when my breath sort of hitched, he being so unexpected; but right away after I see I warn't scared of him worth bothring about.

He was most fifty, and he looked it. His hair was long and tangled and greasy, and hung down, and you could see his eyes shining through like he was behind vines. It was all black, no gray; so was his long, mixed-up whiskers. There warn't no color in his face, where his face showed; it was white; not like another man's white, but a white to make a body sick, a white to make a body's flesh crawl—a tree-toad white, a fish-belly white. As for his clothes—just rags, that was all. He had one ankle resting on t'other knee; the boot on that foot was busted, and two of his toes stuck through, and he worked them now and then. His hat was laying on the floor—an old black slouch with the top caved in, like a lid.

I stood a-looking at him; he set there a-looking at me, with his chair tilted back a little. I set the candle down. I noticed the window was up; so he had clumb in by the shed. He kept a-looking me all over. By and by he says:

"Starchy clothes—very. You think you're a good deal of a big-bug, *don't* you?"

"Maybe I am, maybe I ain't," I says.

"Don't you give me none o' your lip," says he. "You've put on considerable many frills since I been away. I'll take you down a peg before I get done with you. You're educated, too, they say—can read and write. You think you're better'n your father, now, don't you, because he can't? *I'll* take it out of you. Who told you you might meddle with such hifalut'n foolishness, hey?—who told you you could?'

"The widow. She told me."

"The widow, hey?—and who told the widow she could put in her shovel about a thing that ain't none of her business?"

"Nobody never told her."

"Well, I'll learn her how to meddle. And looky here—you drop that school, you hear? I'll learn people to bring up a boy to put on airs over his own father and let on to be better'n what *he* is. You lemme catch you fooling around that school again, you hear? Your mother couldn't read, and she couldn't write, nuther, before she died. None of the family couldn't before *they* died. *I* can't; and here you're a-swelling yourself up like this. I ain't the man to stand it—you hear? Say, lemme hear you read."

I took up a book and begun something about General Washington and the wars. When I'd read about a half a minute, he fetched the book a whack with his hand and knocked it across the house. He says:

"It's so. You can do it. I had my doubts when you told me. Now looky here; you stop that putting on frills. I won't have it. I'll lay for you, my smarty; and if I catch you about that school I'll tan you good. First you know you'll get religion, too. I never see such a son."

He took up a little blue and yaller picture of some cows and a boy, and says:

"What's this?"

"It's something they give me for learning my lessons good."

He tore it up, and says:

"I'll give you something better—I'll give you a cowhide."

He set there a-mumbling and a-growling a minute, and then he says:

"*Ain't* you a sweet-scented dandy, though? A bed; and bedclothes; and a look'n'-glass; and a piece of carpet on the floor—and your own father got to sleep with the hogs in the tanyard. I never see such a son. I bet I'll take some o' these frills out o' you before I'm done with you. Why, there ain't no end to your airs—they say you're rich. Hey?—how's that?"

"They lie—that's how."

"Looky here—mind how you talk to me; I'm a-standing about all I can stand now—so don't gimme no sass. I've been in town two days, and I hain't heard nothing but about you bein' rich. I heard about it away down the river, too. That's why I come. You git me that money to-morrow—I want it."

"I hain't got no money."

"It's a lie. Judge Thatcher's got it. You git it. I want it."

"I hain't got no money, I tell you. You ask Judge Thatcher; he'll tell you the same."

"All right. I'll ask him; and I'll make him pungle, too, or I'll know the reason why. Say, how much you got in your pocket? I want it."

"I hain't got only a dollar, and I want that to——"

"It don't make no difference what you want it for—you just shell it out."

He took it and bit it to see if it was good, and then he said he was going down-town to get some whisky; said he hadn't had a drink all day. When he had got out on the shed he put his head in again, and cussed me for putting on frills and trying to be better than him; and when I reckoned he was gone he come back and put his head in again, and told me to mind about that school, because he was going to lay for me and lick me if I didn't drop that.

Next day he was drunk, and he went to Judge Thatcher's and bullyragged him, and tried to make him give up the money; but he couldn't, and then he swore he'd make the law force him.

The judge and the widow went to law to get the court to take me away from him and let one of them be my guardian; but it was a new judge that had just come, and he didn't know the old man; so he said courts mustn't interfere and separate families if they could help it; said he'd druther not take a child away from its father. So Judge Thatcher and the widow had to quit on the business.

That pleased the old man till he couldn't rest. He said he'd cowhide me till I was black and blue if I didn't raise some money for him. I borrowed three dollars from Judge Thatcher, and pap took it and got drunk, and went a-blowing around and cussing and whooping and carrying on; and he kept it up all over town, with a tin pan, till most midnight; then they jailed him, and next day they had him before court, and jailed him again for a week. But he said *he* was satisfied; said he was boss of his son, and he'd make it warm for *him*.

When he got out the new judge said he was a-going to make a man of him. So he took him to his own house, and dressed him up clean and nice, and had him to breakfast and dinner and supper with the family, and was just old pie to him, so to speak. And after supper he talked to him about temperance and such things till the old man cried, and said he'd been a fool, and fooled away his life; but now he was a-going to turn over a new leaf and be a man nobody wouldn't be ashamed of, and he hoped the judge would help him and not look down on him. The judge said he could hug him for them words; so *he* cried, and his wife she cried again; pap said he'd been a man that had always been misunderstood before, and the judge said he believed it. The old man said that what a man wanted that was down was sympathy, and the judge said it was so; so they cried again. And when it was bedtime the old man rose up and held out his hand, and says:

"Look at it, gentlemen and ladies all; take a-hold of it; shake it. There's a hand that was the hand of a hog; but it ain't so no more; it's the hand of a man that's started in on a new life, and'll die before he'll go back. You mark them words—don't forget I said them. It's a clean hand now; shake it—don't be afeard."

So they shook it, one after the other, all around, and cried. The judge's wife she kissed it. Then the old man he signed a pledge—made his mark. The judge said it was the holiest time on record, or something like that. Then they tucked the old man into a beautiful room, which was the spare room, and in the night some time he got powerful thirsty and clumb out on to the porch-roof and slid down a stanchion and traded his new coat for a jug of forty-rod, and clumb back again and had a good old time; and toward daylight he crawled out again, drunk as a fiddler, and rolled off the porch and broke his left arm in two places, and was most froze to death when somebody found him after sun-up. And when they come to look at that spare room they had to take soundings before they could navigate it.

The judge he felt kind of sore. He said he reckoned a body could reform the old man with a shotgun, maybe, but he didn't know no other way.

Father's birthday. He would have been 96, 96, yes, today; and could have been 96 like other people one has known, but mercifully was not. His life would have utterly ended mine.

VIRGINIA WOOLF

*   *

. . . anybody can take a little pushing . . .

MARK VAN DOREN
Grandison and Son

Nobody could love Barlow more than he did, and yet he had these dreams about him. His own son, and he dreamed almost every night of how he came in first. There was a race, and many runners, but Barlow always came in first.

Last night the course was circular—no, oval, like a track for horses. It was a race track—he remembered everything now—with grandstands and a little tower for the starters, and another one, just like it, for the judges. The crowd stood up and looked through thousands of binoculars—he recalled how the sun struck them once and they glittered as if they were the countless eyes of one gigantic creature: a fly, magnified until it filled the far half of the world. And down on the track a dozen runners, looking very small, sprinted around the last curve toward the finish line. But they were men, not horses: young men, and Barlow led them all the way. He had not started in the lead, but there was no doubt of it now. Here he came, his head up, smiling, his shoulders flashing in the sun. His knees effortlessly pumped the air, and his feet flew over the brown dusty ground. The others were not far behind; they followed like a kind of audience, marveling; they were happy because he won. He did win, of course; and the entire grandstand shook with joy. Doubtless there was shouting—"Barlow! Barlow! Barlow!"—but the dream suppressed the sound. So did it suppress any scene of father and son together, shaking hands, when the event was over. None of these dreams ever ended that way. The contest was far off, and Barlow had it to himself. He ran like one alone, and kept on going after he had crossed the line. He kept on as toward another race—on and on, growing smaller every second, till there was a final flash of sun upon his shoulders and he passed out of the dream. And Grandison woke up.

"Why shouldn't Barlow win?" asked Mrs. Grandison. "It's a fine dream to have, and you should be proud. Why aren't you, I wonder?"

He could never explain. He shouldn't have told her—and wouldn't have; except that tonight the burden was heavier on his heart than it had been before. He was glad she had gone to her room without waiting to learn why he wasn't proud. She often left him like that, demanding reasons she refused to hear. An annoying habit—many women had it—but tonight it was convenient. He could never explain, even to an ideal listener.

He sat in his deep chair by the standing lamp and thought of other races he had seen Barlow run. Once he was an Indian, naked to the waist—there was a wide slope of prairie grass ascending to a long, low ridge beyond which the sun was setting, and over that ridge a score of young braves thrust their black smooth heads, their fierce faces. They were already running, but now this was the final stretch. Where the shadow of the ridge ended in a dark line on the plain—and yet it was a moving line, for the sun dropped rapidly, and the area of shade spread eastward at the same rate— the runners beheld their prize, a live eagle tethered to a stake. Thongs about its feet reduced it to a wilder thing than it had ever been in the sky. It raged as if its wrath were the wrath of all the living gods, and thrashed the green ground with wings whose finest feathers would soon be but shredded fragments of themselves. Here came the racers, though, and one of them, should he be strong enough to bear the bird away, would save the plumes for a headdress that tomorrow would show who had been victor. The young chief in front doubtless possessed the necessary strength. Strange, too, for his hair was not glossy black, and his nose and chin—why, he was Barlow! Unknown to the others, here came Barlow, and he covered the last hundred yards with no such effort as they put forth. He looked neither this way nor that, but

skimmed the prairie grass as if his feet were lighter than its tops—
looking straight ahead and laughing as at last he reached and
caught the eagle, stake, thongs and all, and kept on going, on and
on, the great wings beating about his head until both he and the
bird disappeared into the wall of gold light the sun had built
among the horizon clouds. Had they left the ground, were they
soaring as they went out of sight? That couldn't be determined at
this distance, where the losers in the race stood in a close band,
admiring, and the father of the winner, invisible at their side,
wished he could claim that his son had seen him as he passed. But
he knew he hadn't. Somewhere now he was speeding toward another field where on another day, another night, he would come
in first, his head high, laughing without sound.

This was perhaps a month ago—Grandison wasn't sure just
when, for he kept no chronology. It may have been before or
after the footrace at Corinth, where the reward of Barlow's winning was a dark green wreath, a semicircle of laurel. But no
sooner was it placed upon his head than off he flew, straight over
the sea, and left nothing by which he could be identified except
a wake of foam, half in the waves and half in the blue air, that
hung a short while like the mist a goddess wears when she comes
down among mortals. Certainly the next night brought him to
Verona, where instead of a wreath he bore away a green cloth,
with bright gold about its edges. There was no telling what the
scenery might be, or who the persons. Once it was a track meet,
with the contestants in snow-white shorts and sleeveless shirts;
and across each of their chests a colored ribbon descended, saying
the name of his school. Grandison, in the windy bleachers that
were too high for any of the athletes to distinguish one spectator
from another, himself could not make out the letters on Barlow's
costume. The colors, green and gold, were all he saw; and the
triumphant moment when the last hurdle was cleared and the
tape broken. The officials drew quickly together, studying their
watches. It was a record for two hundred and twenty yards; and
the announcement of this brought thunder from the seats across
the field from where Grandison sat in the cool sun, in the brisk
wind. But Barlow was even then where no referee or reporter
could find him. He had rounded the stadium without stopping,
and for all his father knew he was streaking through the park that

lay between here and the business section. Grandison never settled the question, of course, for the dream was over and Barlow was out of it, running against time lest he be late for the next one.

There had been nights when the race was not easy to interpret as a race. There was no running, no track or roadway, and no goal. At least it was a contest, and Barlow won. A bridge was being planned to cross the widest river in the world—and the deepest, judging by these gray cliffs all around, and the narrow water, far, far down like a yellow chalk mark, meandering. There was no bridge yet, this was merely the place where it would be. Nearby, however, was a low building, with many corridors and rooms, where youthful engineers sat figuring and drawing, their heads bent ever lower as the columns of their calculation lengthened. Days passed, and white-haired men—master engineers—came and went, inspecting what the young men had before them on their tables. Then suddenly, one evening when the sun had set and lavender ceiling lights had been turned on, the eldest of the inspectors, glancing down, gave a cry and called his colleagues to him. Here at last was the design. The bridge could now be built. This young man had solved the problem of problems. And who was he but Barlow?

Scholars in black robes bent over books in cubicles, mumbling the beautiful lines which they must memorize if they were to become ambassadors and viceroys. The best among them would be companion to the emperor, and have uncounted wealth at his hourly disposal. The best would be the one who at the Spring Reading could recite without an error, and with perfect inflection, the entire corpus of ancient poetry—the wisdom of his race, and its chief ornament. When the gong sounded, and the pale students, unlocked from their little rooms, assembled for the reading, all of them save one stumbled at the line about the waterfall. It was a line that fell itself, syllable by syllable, and splashed in a final sound of breath-stopping subtlety. Only one scholar spoke it truly; and was proclaimed; and he was Barlow.

Attorneys argued in court; politicians shouted from platforms; preachers, thoughtless of promotion—but all of them were watched, and one of them would be made bishop—intoned their doctrine in high pulpits; young officers, infants of the staff, ran to do the bidding of the general; and in each competition Barlow came out first. Easily, too, and smiling, and never knowing who it was that dreamed him.

Why then was Grandison not proud?

Before he put the answer he got out of his chair and went into the kitchen for a sandwich and a glass of milk. Or no, sherry. He would find that back in the sideboard; so he cut the bread and the meat, placed them properly together, and on the way into the living room again picked an apple off a dish. It would do for dessert. He was having a meal at midnight, sweet and all.

But he doubted the apple after he had sat down, and took an investigative bite. There was a worm under the skin, just where he had bitten. He threw the whole thing into the fireplace; it struck one of the andirons, and pieces of it flew off as if some inner force had expelled them. A rotten thing, he said, and reconsidered the sherry. Whisky was better. Without any water, either.

Why was he not proud? Because of what he had made of Barlow.

He knew this very well, but he didn't know how to tell anybody, least of all the boy's mother. Barlow was still a boy, and he shouldn't be. He was afraid of everything; but particularly, he was afraid of his father who loved him so much. He was afraid of disappointing him.

God knows, said Grandison to himself, watching the wet stain the apple had left on the black knob of the andiron, anybody can take a little pushing—I got it from *my* father, and I'm glad I did. Why didn't it work with Barlow then? I started too soon; I overdid it; I let him see too clearly how much difference it would make to me if he wasn't best in everything. Is that it? Is any of those the reason? Damn it, I don't know. I only know how he behaves. The first time he hid his report card—that was when I might have known. But I didn't; I gave him thunder for not showing me the card—a pretty good one, too. He never played games. I got him that expensive mitt so he could be equal with the other boys. It sunk him; he could never come up to it. It wasn't stolen as he said, I know it wasn't, he hid it too, or threw it in the river. I should have had more sense about those girls of his. They seemed infants to me, and I said so, always on the theory that soon enough he would find a grown young woman to bring home. And now he's in the firm. But he avoids my office as if the air of it would poison him. He lunches with file clerks and is late to conference. No female file clerks, either. So far as I know he hasn't looked at a woman in three years.

And now I have these dreams. I stopped pushing him by day, or thought I did, but I can't stop at night. I've let him alone to the limit. I've been as casual with him as I would be if he were Tom Bullwin's son, or Jake Friend's—anybody's but mine. I'm sure I don't sound anxious, or seem to have plans. By day, that is, or evenings when he's home. I didn't even ask him where he was going this week he had off. I wonder where. But I didn't ask.

It isn't as if he were sullen, or seemed to hate me. He's nice. Barlow's a nice boy.

I don't believe I can stand another dream. They break my heart —that serious, nice boy who would like it if no one ever looked his way—if he hadn't been born, even—laughing as he comes in first. Then running on to do it again. That's the worst part. I called him once, I said to come back, but he didn't hear. Clara didn't either—I woke her up and asked her.

Of course you don't make any noise in dreams, at least in this kind that comes every night. Or almost every night.

He was momentarily cheered by the thought that this night there might be no dream, and got up at once to go to bed.

But the smooth pillow, and the covers folded back, terrified him as much as ever. It was like being lowered into a grave that waited, waited, waited to reveal the secrets no man knows till he lies down for the last time.

It was even worse.

Grandison went to sleep almost at once and saw the earth sailing above him—serenely, serenely sailing through black space in which it was the only light. It was not very big and not very far away; but all of it was there, he saw it in the round, and saw how it softly, softly pushed its way, turning slowly all the time, straight on into a blackness which itself was soft, a satin atmosphere that gave way in gentle folds as it was penetrated. The earth turned slowly all the time, and showed its parts—its continents, countries, counties, oceans, lakes, and ponds—as if it were proud of their variety. They all seemed lighted from within; thin lines, like veins upon the surface of an egg, separated them from one another, and yet they were as one because their faint colors blended so perfectly, like the pure tints in mother of pearl.

Something was about to happen, though.

He looked again, and the boundary lines had thickened—were becoming cracks through which light poured—no, fire, white fire —were gulfs of darkness, finally, between shining segments of the sphere that sailed off, each on its separate course, into the dense black ahead.

The inner fire was spent. The upheaval, occurring without sound, was now a piece of the same silent history that had been repeating itself here forever. Only the segments sailed on, each one of them a jagged remnant of the smooth sphere it once belonged to, each one of them engaged now in a race to be the first—

A race—to be the first—

Grandison looked still again and saw that each flying portion of what had been a world was piloted by someone—a young man —who leaned out of it and gazed into the dark.

And the one in front was Barlow—laughing at the black wind on his cheeks, afraid yet not afraid. Doing what he must do, anyway. Piloting his remnant. He was the first one; he faced all outer darkness and was not afraid.

Then Barlow turned and saw Grandison. Never before had he done so, but now he did. And tears filled his eyes as he wept for joy, knowing that his father witnessed the not-to-be-doubted triumph of this moment.

Or did he know? Perhaps the distance was too great, for his gaze faltered and all the confidence went out of it. Could he really see this far? Grandison grimaced and gestured—held his hands over his head and clasped them—smiled as widely as he could smile, and nodded grotesquely, till his neck hurt and his brains addled. Still Barlow seemed uncertain; agony strained his eyes, and his chin quivered.

"Barlow! Good boy! Barlow, I can see you! Wonderful! Good boy!" Grandison shouted and shouted. But he couldn't even hear himself. The immense spaces swallowed every sound. In any event there was no visible effect on Barlow.

Then Barlow fell—not as a spark does, shot from the fire, or as a stone does, plunging, but like a feather, helplessly, fluttering slowly down and down, veering and tacking with each slightest current, yet slipping further down and down, descending each second into darkness that prophesied at last some utter darkness where perhaps no object even fell, but lay suspended as planks of ships do in the deepest ocean.

Clara shook her husband, then shook him again, harder. Would he ever wake up?

He did not do so till she screamed.

"What's the matter?" he asked, sitting up suddenly, his forehead gleaming with sweat.

"You ask that." Clara dropped down by him, crying. "Walter, I was afraid—I heard you calling Barlow's name, and it sounded as if he were in trouble—as if he were drowning, maybe, or lost somewhere. What was it. Walter! Tell me!"

Grandison wished he could.

"It wasn't anything," he said. "Only another nightmare. I'll stop having them some day—I promise."

"How can you promise such a thing? They keep coming. How can you promise?"

"I'm sorry, dear. I'll do my best. Now you go back to bed."

"But will you be all right? I don't like to leave you."

"I'm tired, dear, and so are you. Goodnight. There won't be any more this time, I'm sure of that."

There couldn't be, he said to himself as Clara's door closed and the light it had let in died across the room. There wasn't any more. Perhaps this was the end.

He covered himself carefully and turned on his right side. Perhaps it was the promised end.

*　　　*

Where one has not had a good father, one must create one.
FRIEDRICH WILHELM NIETZSCHE

*　　　*

I will not marry yet. . . .

WILLIAM SHAKESPEARE

from

ROMEO AND JULIET: ACT THREE, SCENE FIVE

LADY CAPULET *But now I'll tell thee joyful tidings girl.*
JULIET *And joy comes well in such a needy time.*
What are they, I beseech your ladyship?
LADY CAPULET *Well, well, thou hast a careful father child,*
One who to put thee from thy heaviness,
Hath sorted out a sudden day of joy,
That thou expects not, nor I looked not for.
JULIET *Madam, in happy time, what day is that?*
LADY CAPULET *Marry, my child, early next Thursday morn,*
The gallant, young, and noble gentleman,
The County Paris, at Saint Peter's Church,
Shall happily make thee there a joyful bride.
JULIET *Now by Saint Peter's Church, and Peter too,*
He shall not make me there a joyful bride.
I wonder at this haste, that I must wed
Ere he that should be husband comes to woo.
I pray you tell my lord and father, madam,
I will not marry yet, and when I do, I swear
It shall be Romeo, whom you know I hate,
Rather than Paris. These are news indeed.
LADY CAPULET *Here comes your father, tell him so yourself;*
And see how he will take it at your hands.
Enter Capulet and Nurse.
CAPULET *When the sun sets, the earth doth drizzle dew;*
But for the sunset of my brother's son
It rains downright.
How now, a conduit, girl? What, still in tears?
Evermore showering? In one little body
Thou counterfeits a bark, a sea, a wind.
For still thy eyes, which I may call the sea,
Do ebb and flow with tears; the bark thy body is,
Sailing in this salt flood; the winds, thy sighs,

Who, raging with thy tears, and they with them,
Without a sudden calm, will overset
Thy tempest-tossed body. How now wife,
Have you delivered to her our decree?

LADY CAPULET *Ay sir, but she will none, she gives you thanks,*
I would the fool were married to her grave.

CAPULET *Soft, take me with you, take me with you wife.*
How will she none? Doth she not give us thanks?
Is she not proud? Doth she not count her blessed,
Unworthy as she is, that we have wrought
So worthy a gentleman to be her bridegroom?

JULIET *Not proud you have, but thankful that you have.*
Proud can I never be of what I hate,
But thankful even for hate, that is meant love.

CAPULET *How now! how now, chop-logic, what is this?*
Proud, and, I thank you, and, I thank you not;
And yet, not proud—mistress minion you,
Thank me no thankings, nor proud me no prouds,
But fettle your fine joints 'gainst Thursday next,
To go with Paris to Saint Peter's Church;
Or I will drag thee on a hurdle thither.
Out you green-sickness carrion, out you baggage,
You tallow-face!

LADY CAPULET *Fie, fie, what, are you mad?*

JULIET *Good father, I beseech you on my knees,*
Hear me with patience, but to speak a word.

CAPULET *Hang thee young baggage, disobedient wretch!*
I tell thee what, get thee to church a Thursday,
Or never after look me in the face.
Speak not, reply not, do not answer me.
My fingers itch. Wife, we scarce thought us blessed,
That God had lent us but this only child;
But now I see this one is one too much,
And that we have a curse in having her.
Out on her, hilding!

NURSE *God in heaven bless her.*
You are to blame my lord to rate her so.

CAPULET *And why, my lady wisdom? Hold your tongue.*
Good Prudence, smatter with your gossips, go.

NURSE *I speak no treason.*

CAPULET *O God ye god-den.*

NURSE *May not one speak?*

CAPULET *Peace you mumbling fool.*
  Utter your gravity o'er a gossip's bowl,
  For here we need it not.
LADY CAPULET *You are too hot.*
CAPULET *God's bread, it makes me mad.*
  Day, night, hour; tide, time; work, play;
  Alone, in company; still my care hath been
  To have her matched; and having now provided
  A gentleman of princely parentage,
  Of fair demesnes, youthful and nobly trained,
  Stuffed as they say with honourable parts,
  Proportioned as one's thought would wish a man—
  And then to have a wretched puling fool,
  A whining mammet, in her fortune's tender,
  To answer, I'll not wed, I cannot love,
  I am too young, I pray you pardon me—
  But, an you will not wed, I'll pardon you.
  Graze where you will, you shall not house with me.
  Look to't, I do not use to jest.
  Thursday is near, lay hand on heart, advise.
  An you be mine, I'll give you to my friend;
  An you be not, hang, beg, starve, die in the streets,
  For by my soul, I'll ne'er acknowledge thee,
  Nor what is mine shall never do thee good.
  Trust to't, bethink you. I'll not be forsworn. . . .

*   *

You wouldn't like my family.

MORLEY CALLAGHAN
THE SNOB

IT WAS AT THE BOOK COUNTER in the department store that John
Harcourt, the student, caught a glimpse of his father. At first he
could not be sure in the crowd that pushed along the aisle, but
there was something about the colour of the back of the elderly
man's neck, something about the faded felt hat, that he knew very

well. Harcourt was standing with the girl he loved, buying a book for her. All afternoon he had been talking to her, eagerly, but with an anxious diffidence, as if there still remained in him an innocent wonder that she should be delighted to be with him. From underneath her wide-brimmed straw hat, her face, so fair and beautifully strong with its expression of cool independence, kept turning up to him and sometimes smiled at what he said. That was the way they always talked, never daring to show much full, strong feeling. Harcourt had just bought the book, and had reached into his pocket for the money with a free, ready gesture to make it appear that he was accustomed to buying books for young ladies, when the white-haired man in the faded felt hat, at the other end of the counter, turned half toward him, and Harcourt knew he was standing only a few feet away from his father.

The young man's easy words trailed away and his voice became little more than a whisper, as if he were afraid that everyone in the store might recognize it. There was rising in him a dreadful uneasiness; something very precious that he wanted to hold seemed close to destruction. His father, standing at the end of the bargain counter, was planted squarely on his two feet, turning a book over thoughtfully in his hands. Then he took out his glasses from an old, worn leather case and adjusted them on the end of his nose, looking down over them at the book. His coat was thrown open, two buttons on his vest were undone, his gray hair was too long, and in his rather shabby clothes he looked very much like a working-man, a carpenter perhaps. Such a resentment rose in young Harcourt that he wanted to cry out bitterly, "Why does he dress as if he never owned a decent suit in his life? He doesn't care what the whole world thinks of him. He never did. I've told him a hundred times he ought to wear his good clothes when he goes out. Mother's told him the same thing. He just laughs. And now Grace may see him. Grace will meet him."

So young Harcourt stood still, with his head down, feeling that something very painful was impending. Once he looked anxiously at Grace, who had turned to the bargain counter. Among those people drifting aimlessly by with hot red faces, getting in each other's way, using their elbows but keeping their faces detached and wooden, she looked tall and splendidly alone. She was so sure of herself, her relation to the people in the aisles, the clerks behind the counter, the books on the shelves, and everything around her. Still keeping his head down and moving close, he whispered uneasily, "Let's go and have tea somewhere, Grace."

"In a minute, dear," she said.

"Let's go now."

"In just a minute, dear," she repeated absently.

"There's not a breath of air in here. Let's go now."

"What makes you so impatient?"

"There's nothing but old books on that counter."

"There may be something here I've wanted all my life," she said, smiling at him brightly and not noticing the uneasiness in his face.

So Harcourt had to move slowly behind her, getting closer to his father all the time. He could feel the space that separated them narrowing. Once he looked up with a vague, sidelong glance. But his father, red-faced and happy, was still reading the book, only now there was a meditative expression on his face, as if something in the book had stirred him and he intended to stay there reading for some time.

Old Harcourt had lots of time to amuse himself, because he was on a pension after working hard all his life. He had sent John to the university and he was eager to have him distinguish himself. Every night when John came home, whether it was early or late, he used to go into his father's and mother's bedroom and turn on the light and talk to them about the interesting things that had happened to him during the day. They listened and shared this new world with him. They both sat up in their night-clothes and, while his mother asked all the questions, his father listened attentively with his head cocked on one side and a smile or a frown on his face. The memory of all this was in John now, and there was also a desperate longing and a pain within him growing harder to bear as he glanced fearfully at his father, but he thought stubbornly, "I can't introduce him. It'll be easier for everybody if he doesn't see us. I'm not ashamed. But it will be easier. It'll be more sensible. It'll only embarrass him to see Grace." By this time he knew he was ashamed, but he felt that his shame was justified, for Grace's father had the smooth, confident manner of a man who had lived all his life among people who were rich and sure of themselves. Often when he had been in Grace's home talking politely to her mother, John had kept on thinking of the plainness of his own home and of his parents' laughing, good-natured untidiness, and he resolved desperately that he must make Grace's people admire him.

He looked up cautiously, for they were about eight feet away from his father, but at that moment his father, too, looked up and John's glance shifted swiftly far over the aisle, over the counters, seeing nothing. As his father's blue, calm eyes stared steadily over the glasses, there was an instant when their glances might have met. Neither one could have been certain, yet John, as he turned away and began to talk to Grace hurriedly, knew surely that his father had seen him. He knew it by the steady calmness in his father's blue eyes. John's shame grew, and then humiliation sickened him as he waited and did nothing.

His father turned away, going down the aisle, walking erectly in his shabby clothes, his shoulders very straight, never once looking back. His father would walk slowly along the street, he knew, with that meditative expression deepening and becoming grave.

Young Harcourt stood beside Grace, brushing against her soft shoulder, and made faintly aware again of the delicate scent she used. There, so close beside him, she was holding within her everything he wanted to reach out for, only now he felt a sharp hostility that made him sullen and silent.

"You were right, John," she was drawling in her soft voice. "It does get unbearable in here on a hot day. Do let's go now. Have you ever noticed that department stores after a time can make you really hate people?" But she smiled when she spoke, so he might see that she really hated no one.

"You don't like people, do you?" he said sharply.

"People? What people? What do you mean?"

"I mean," he went on irritably, "you don't like the kind of people you bump into here, for example."

"Not especially. Who does? What are you talking about?"

"Anybody could see you don't," he said recklessly, full of a savage eagerness to hurt her. "I say you don't like simple, honest people, the kind of people you meet all over the city." He blurted the words out as if he wanted to shake her, but he was longing to say, "You wouldn't like my family. Why couldn't I take you home to have dinner with them? You'd turn up your nose at them, because they've no pretensions. As soon as my father saw you, he knew you wouldn't want to meet him. I could tell by the way he turned."

His father was on his way home now, he knew, and that evening at dinner they would meet. His mother and sister would talk rapidly, but his father would say nothing to him, or to anyone. There would only be Harcourt's memory of the level look in the blue eyes, and the knowledge of his father's pain as he walked away.

Grace watched John's gloomy face as they walked through the store, and she knew he was nursing some private rage, and so her own resentment and exasperation kept growing, and she said crisply, "You're entitled to your moods on a hot afternoon, I suppose, but if I feel I don't like it here, then I don't like it. You wanted to go yourself. Who likes to spend very much time in a department store on a hot afternoon? I begin to hate every stupid person that bangs into me, everybody near me. What does that make me?"

"It makes you a snob."

"So I'm a snob now?" she said angrily.

"Certainly you're a snob," he said. They were at the door and going out to the street. As they walked in the sunlight, in the crowd moving slowly down the street, he was groping for words to describe the secret thoughts he had always had about her. "I've always known how you'd feel about people I like who didn't fit into your private world," he said.

"You're a very stupid person," she said. Her face was flushed now, and it was hard for her to express her indignation, so she stared straight ahead as she walked along.

They had never talked in this way, and now they were both quickly eager to hurt each other. With a flow of words, she started to argue with him, then she checked herself and said calmly, "Listen, John, I imagine you're tired of my company. There's no sense in having tea together. I think I'd better leave you right here."

"That's fine," he said. "Good afternoon."

"Good-by."

"Good-by."

She started to go, she had gone two paces, but he reached out desperately and held her arm, and he was frightened, and pleading, "Please don't go, Grace."

All the anger and irritation had left him; there was just a desperate anxiety in his voice as he pleaded, "Please forgive me. I've no right to talk to you like that. I don't know why I'm so rude or what's the matter. I'm ridiculous. I'm very, very ridiculous. Please, you must forgive me. Don't leave me."

He had never talked to her so brokenly, and his sincerity, the depth of his feeling, began to stir her. While she listened, feeling all the yearning in him, they seemed to have been brought closer together, by opposing each other, than ever before, and she began to feel almost shy. "I don't know what's the matter. I suppose we're both irritable. It must be the weather," she said. "But I'm not angry, John."

He nodded his head miserably. He longed to tell her that he was sure she would have been charming to his father, but he had never felt so wretched in his life. He held her arm tight, as if he must hold it or what he wanted most in the world would slip away from him, yet he kept thinking, as he would ever think, of his father walking away quietly with his head never turning.

HUSBAND

*No man is entirely responsible for his father.
That is his mother's affair.*

Margaret Turnbull: from Alabaster Lamps

. . . then with awful daring . . . he asks my mother to marry him . . .

DELMORE SCHWARTZ
IN DREAMS BEGIN RESPONSIBILITIES

I

I THINK it is the year 1909. I feel as if I were in a motion picture theatre, the long arm of light crossing the darkness and spinning, my eyes fixed on the screen. This is a silent picture as if an old Biograph one, in which the actors are dressed in ridiculously old-fashioned clothes, and one flash succeeds another with sudden jumps. The actors too seem to jump about and walk too fast. The shots themselves are full of dots and rays, as if it were raining when the picture was photographed. The light is bad.

It is Sunday afternoon, June 12th, 1909, and my father is walking down the quiet streets of Brooklyn on his way to visit my mother. His clothes are newly pressed and his tie is too tight in his high collar. He jingles the coins in his pockets, thinking of the witty things he will say. I feel as if I had by now relaxed entirely in the soft darkness of the theatre; the organist peals out the obvious and approximate emotions on which the audience rocks unknowingly. I am anonymous, and I have forgotten myself. It is always so when one goes to the movies, it is, as they say, a drug.

My father walks from street to street of trees, lawns and houses, once in a while coming to an avenue on which a streetcar skates and gnaws, slowly progressing. The conductor, who has a handle-bar mustache, helps a young lady wearing a hat like a bowl with feathers on to the car. She lifts her long skirts slightly as she mounts the steps. He leisurely makes change and rings his bell. It is obviously Sunday, for everyone is wearing Sunday clothes, and the street-car's noises emphasize the quiet of the holiday. Is not Brooklyn the City of Churches? The shops are closed and their shades drawn, but for an occasional stationery store or drug-store with great green balls in the window.

My father has chosen to take this long walk because he likes to walk and think. He thinks about himself in the future and so arrives at the place he is to visit in a state of mild exaltation. He pays no attention to the houses he is passing, in which the Sunday dinner is being eaten, nor to the many trees which patrol each street, now coming to their full leafage and the time when they will room the whole street in cool shadow. An occasional carriage passes, the horse's hooves falling like stones in the quiet afternoon, and once in a while an automobile, looking like an enormous upholstered sofa, puffs and passes.

My father thinks of my mother, of how nice it will be to introduce her to his family. But he is not yet sure that he wants to marry her, and once in a while he becomes panicky about the bond already established. He reassures himself by thinking of the big men he admires who are married: William Randolph Hearst, and William Howard Taft, who has just become President of the United States.

My father arrives at my mother's house. He has come too early and so is suddenly embarrassed. My aunt, my mother's sister, answers the loud bell with her napkin in her hand, for the family is still at dinner. As my father enters, my grandfather rises from the table and shakes hands with him. My mother has run upstairs to tidy herself. My grandmother asks my father if he has had dinner, and tells him that Rose will be downstairs soon. My grandfather opens the conversation by remarking on the mild June weather. My father sits uncomfortably near the table, holding his hat in his hand. My grandmother tells my aunt to take my father's hat. My uncle, twelve years old, runs into the house, his hair touseled. He shouts a greeting to my father, who has often given him a nickel, and then runs upstairs. It is evident that the respect in which my father is held in this household is tempered by a good deal of mirth. He is impressive, yet he is very awkward.

II

Finally my mother comes downstairs, all dressed up, and my father being engaged in conversation with my grandfather becomes uneasy, not knowing whether to greet my mother or continue the conversation. He gets up from the chair clumsily and says "hello" gruffly. My grandfather watches, examining their congruence, such as it is, with a critical eye, and meanwhile rubbing his bearded cheek roughly, as he always does when he reflects. He is worried; he is afraid that my father will not make a good husband for his oldest daughter. At this point something happens to the film, just as my father is saying something funny to my mother; I am awakened to myself and my unhappiness just as my interest was rising. The audience begins to clap impatiently. Then the trouble is cared for but the film has been returned to a portion just shown, and once more I see my grandfather rubbing his bearded cheek and pondering my father's character. It is difficult to get back into the picture once more and forget myself, but as my mother giggles at my father's words, the darkness drowns me.

My father and mother depart from the house, my father shaking hands with my mother once more, out of some unknown uneasiness. I stir uneasily also, slouched in the hard chair of the theatre. Where is the older uncle, my mother's older brother? He is studying in his bedroom upstairs, studying for his final examination at the College of the City of New York, having been dead of rapid pneumonia for the last twenty-one years. My mother and father walk down the same quiet streets once more. My mother is holding my father's arm and telling him of the novel which she has been reading; and my father utters judgments of the characters as the plot is made clear to him. This is a habit which he very much enjoys, for he feels the utmost superiority and confidence when he approves and condemns the behavior of other people. At times he feels moved to utter a brief "Ugh"—whenever the story becomes what he would call sugary. This tribute is paid to his manliness. My mother feels satisfied by the interest which she has awakened; she is showing my father how intelligent she is, and how interesting.

They reach the avenue, and the street-car leisurely arrives. They are going to Coney Island this afternoon, although my mother considers that such pleasures are inferior. She has made up her mind to indulge only in a walk on the boardwalk and a pleasant dinner, avoiding the riotous amusements as being beneath the dignity of so dignified a couple.

My father tells my mother how much money he has made in the past week, exaggerating an amount which need not have been exaggerated. But my father has always felt that actualities somehow fall short. Suddenly I begin to weep. The determined old lady who sits next to me in the theatre is annoyed and looks at me with an angry face, and being intimidated, I stop. I drag out my handkerchief and dry my face, licking the drop which has fallen near my lips. Meanwhile I have missed something, for here are my mother and father alighting at the last stop, Coney Island.

III

They walk toward the boardwalk, and my father commands my mother to inhale the pungent air from the sea. They both breathe in deeply, both of them laughing as they do so. They have in common a great interest in health, although my father is strong and husky, my mother frail. Their minds are full of theories of what is good to eat and not good to eat, and sometimes they engage in heated discussions of the subject, the whole matter ending in my father's announcement, made with a scornful bluster, that you have to die sooner or later anyway. On the boardwalk's flagpole, the American flag is pulsing in an intermittent wind from the sea.

My father and mother go to the rail of the boardwalk and look down on the beach where a good many bathers are casually walking about. A few are in the surf. A peanut whistle pierces the air with its pleasant and active whine, and my father goes to buy peanuts. My mother remains at the rail and stares at the ocean. The ocean seems merry to her; it pointedly sparkles and again and again the pony waves are released. She notices the children digging in the wet sand, and the bathing costumes of the girls who are her own age. My father returns with the peanuts. Overhead the sun's lightning strikes and strikes, but neither of them is at all aware of it. The boardwalk is full of people dressed in their Sunday clothes and idly strolling. The tide does not reach as far as the boardwalk, and the strollers would feel no danger if it did. My mother and father lean on the rail of the boardwalk and absently stare at the ocean. The ocean is becoming rough; the waves come in slowly, tugging strength from far back. The moment before they somersault, the moment when they arch their backs so beautifully, showing green and white veins amid the black, that moment is intolerable. They finally crack, dashing fiercely upon the sand, actually driving, full force downward, against the sand, bouncing upward and forward, and at last petering out into a small stream which races up the beach and then is recalled. My parents gaze absentmindedly at the ocean, scarcely interested in its harshness. The sun overhead does not disturb them. But I stare at the terrible sun which breaks up sight, and the fatal, merciless, passionate ocean, I forget my parents. I stare fascinated and finally, shocked by the indifference of my father and mother, I burst out weeping once more. The old lady next to me pats me on the shoulder and says, "There, there, all of this is only a movie, young man, only a movie," but I look up once more at the terrifying sun and the terrifying ocean, and being unable to control my tears, I get up and go to the men's room, stumbling over the feet of the other people seated in my row.

IV

When I return, feeling as if I had awakened in the morning sick for lack of sleep, several hours have apparently passed and my parents are riding on the merry-go-round. My father is on a black horse, my mother on a white one, and they seem to be making an eternal circuit for the single purpose of snatching the nickel rings which are attached to the arm of one of the posts. A hand-organ is playing; it is one with the ceaseless circling of the merry-go-round.

For a moment it seems that they will never get off the merry-go-round because it will never stop. I feel like one who looks down on the avenue from the 50th story of a building. But at length they do get off; even the music of the hand-organ has ceased for a moment. My father has acquired ten rings, my mother only two, although it was my mother who really wanted them.

They walk on along the boardwalk as the afternoon descends by imperceptible degrees into the incredible violet of dusk. Everything fades into a relaxed glow, even the ceaseless murmuring from the beach, and the revolutions of the merry-go-round. They look for a place to have dinner. My father suggests the best one on the board-walk and my mother demurs, in accordance with her principles.

However, they do go to the best place, asking for a table near the window, so that they can look out on the boardwalk and the mobile ocean. My father feels omnipotent as he places a quarter in the waiter's hand as he asks for a table. The place is crowded and here too there is music, this time from a kind of string trio. My father orders dinner with a fine confidence.

As the dinner is eaten, my father tells of his plans for the future, and my mother shows with expressive face how interested she is, and how impressed. My father becomes exultant. He is lifted up by the waltz that is being played, and his own future begins to intoxicate him. My father tells my mother that he is going to expand his business, for there is a great deal of money to be made. He wants to settle down. After all, he is twenty-nine, he has lived by himself since he was thirteen, he is making more and more money, and he is envious of his married friends when he visits them in the cozy security of their homes, surrounded, it seems, by the calm domestic pleasures, and by delightful children, and then, as the waltz reaches the moment when all the dancers swing madly, then, then with awful daring, then he asks my mother to marry him, although awkwardly enough and puzzled, even in his excitement, at how he had arrived at the proposal, and she, to make the whole business worse, begins to cry, and my father looks nervously about, not knowing at all what to do now, and my mother says: "It's all I've wanted from the moment I saw you," sobbing, and he finds all of this very difficult, scarcely to his taste, scarcely as he had thought it would be, on his long walks over Brooklyn Bridge in the revery of a fine cigar, and it was then that I stood up in the theatre and shouted: "Don't do it. It's not too late to change your minds, both of you. Nothing good will come of it, only remorse, hatred, scandal, and two children whose characters are monstrous." The whole audience turned to look at me, annoyed, the usher came hurrying down the aisle flashing his searchlight, and the old lady next to me tugged me down into my seat, saying: "Be quiet. You'll be put out, and you paid thirty-five cents to come in." And so I shut my eyes because I could not bear to see what was happening. I sat there quietly.

V

But after a while I begin to take brief glimpses, and at length I watch again with thirsty interest, like a child who wants to maintain his sulk although offered the bribe of candy. My parents are now having their picture taken in a photographer's booth along the boardwalk. The place is shadowed in the mauve light which is apparently necessary. The camera is set to the side on its tripod and looks like a Martian man. The photographer is instructing my parents in how to pose. My father has his arm over my mother's

shoulder, and both of them smile emphatically. The photographer
brings my mother a bouquet of flowers to hold in her hand but
she holds it at the wrong angle. Then the photographer covers
himself with the black cloth which drapes the camera and all that
one sees of him is one protruding arm and his hand which clutches
the rubber ball which he will squeeze when the picture is finally
taken. But he is not satisfied with their appearance. He feels with
certainty that somehow there is something wrong in their pose.
Again and again he issues from his hidden place with new directions. Each suggestion merely makes matters worse. My father
is becoming impatient. They try a seated pose. The photographer
explains that he has pride, he is not interested in all of this for the
money, he wants to make beautiful pictures. My father says:
"Hurry up, will you? We haven't got all night." But the photographer only scurries about apologetically, and issues new directions.
The photographer charms me. I approve of him with all my heart,
for I know just how he feels, and as he criticizes each revised pose
according to some unknown idea of rightness, I become quite hopeful. But then my father says angrily: "Come on, you've had enough
time, we're not going to wait any longer." And the photographer,
sighing unhappily, goes back under his black covering, holds out
his hand, says: "One, two, three, Now!", and the picture is taken,
with my father's smile turned to a grimace and my mother's bright
and false. It takes a few minutes for the picture to be developed
and as my parents sit in the curious light they become quite depressed.

VI

They have passed a fortune-teller's booth, and my mother wishes
to go in, but my father does not. They begin to argue about it.
My mother becomes stubborn, my father once more impatient,
and then they begin to quarrel, and what my father would like to
do is walk off and leave my mother there, but he knows that that
would never do. My mother refuses to budge. She is near to tears,
but she feels an uncontrollable desire to hear what the palm-reader
will say. My father consents angrily, and they both go into a booth
which is in a way like the photographer's, since it is draped in
black cloth and its light is shadowed. The place is too warm, and
my father keeps saying this is all nonsense, pointing to the crystal

ball on the table. The fortune-teller, a fat, short woman, garbed
in what is supposed to be Oriental robes, comes into the room
from the back and greets them, speaking with an accent. But suddenly my father feels that the whole thing is intolerable; he tugs
at my mother's arm, but my mother refuses to budge. And then,
in terrible anger, my father lets go of my mother's arm and strides
out, leaving my mother stunned. She moves to go after my father,
but the fortune-teller holds her arm tightly and begs her not to do
so, and I in my seat am shocked more than can ever be said, for
I feel as if I were walking a tight-rope a hundred feet over a circus-
audience and suddenly the rope is showing signs of breaking, and
I get up from my seat and begin to shout once more the first words
I can think of to communicate my terrible fear and once more the
usher comes hurrying down the aisle flashing his searchlight, and
the old lady pleads with me, and the shocked audience has turned
to stare at me, and I keep shouting: "What are they doing? Don't
they know what they are doing? Why doesn't my mother go after
my father? If she does not do that, what will she do? Doesn't my
father know what he is doing?"—But the usher has seized my arm
and is dragging me away, and as he does so, he says: "What are
you doing? Don't you know that you can't do whatever you want
to do? Why should a young man like you, with your whole life
before you, get hysterical like this? Why don't you *think* of what
you're doing? You can't act like this even if other people aren't
around! You will be sorry if you do not do what you should do,
you can't carry on like this, it is not right, you will find that out
soon enough, everything you do matters too much," and he said
that dragging me through the lobby of the theatre into the cold
light, and I woke up into the bleak winter morning of my 21st
birthday, the windowsill shining with its lip of snow, and the
morning already begun.

*   *

Three children, five persons, seven years.

JOHN UPDIKE
WIFE-WOOING

OH MY LOVE. Yes. Here we sit, on warm broad floor boards, before a fire, the children between us, in a crescent, eating. The girl and I share one half-pint of French-fried potatoes; you and the boy share another; and in the center, sharing nothing, making simple reflections within himself like a jewel, the baby, mounted in an Easy-baby, sucks at his bottle with frowning mastery, his selfish, contemplative eyes stealing glitter from the center of the flames. And you. You. You allow your skirt, the same black skirt in which this morning you with woman's soft bravery mounted a bicycle and sallied forth to play hymns in difficult keys on the Sunday school's old piano—you allow this black skirt to slide off your raised knees down your thighs, slide *up* your thighs in your body's absolute geography, so the parallel whiteness of their undersides is exposed to the fire's warmth and to my sight. Oh. There is a line of Joyce. I try to recover it from the legendary, imperfectly explored grottoes of *Ulysses*: a garter snapped, to please Blazes Boylan, in a deep Dublin den. What? Smackwarm. That was the crucial word. Smacked smackwarm on her smackable warm woman's thigh. Something like that. A splendid man, to feel that. Smackwarm woman's. Splendid also to feel the curious and potent, inexplicable and irrefutably magical life language leads within itself. What soul took thought and knew that adding "wo" to man would make a woman? The difference exactly. The wide w, the receptive o. Womb. In our crescent the children for all their size seem to come out of you toward me, wet fingers and eyes, tinted bronze. Three children, five persons, seven years. Seven years since I wed wide warm woman, white-thighed. Wooed and wed. Wife. A knife of a word that for all its final bite did not end the wooing. To my wonderment.

We eat meat, meat I wrested warm from the raw hands of the hamburger girl in the diner a mile away, a ferocious place, slick with savagery, wild with chrome; young predators snarling dirty jokes menaced me, old men reached for me with coffee-warmed paws; I wielded my wallet, and won my way back. The fat brown bag of buns was warm beside me in the cold car; the smaller bag holding the two tiny cartons of French-fries emitted an even more urgent heat. Back through the black winter air to the fire, the intimate cave, where halloos and hurrahs greeted me, the deer, mouth agape and its cotton throat gushing, stretched dead across my shoulders. And now you, beside the white O of the plate upon which the children discarded with squeals of disgust the rings of translucent onion that came squeezed in the hamburgers—you push your toes an inch closer to the blaze, and the ashy white of the inside of your deep thigh is lazily laid bare, and the eternally elastic garter snaps smackwarm against my hidden heart.

Who would have thought, wide wife, back there in the white tremble of the ceremony (in the corner of my eye I held, despite the distracting hail of ominous vows, the vibration of the cluster of stephanotis clutched against your waist), that seven years would bring us no distance, through all those warm beds, to the same trembling point, of beginning? The cells change every seven years, and down in the atom, apparently, there is a strange discontinuity; as if God wills the universe anew every instant. (Ah God, dear God, tall friend of my childhood, I will never forget you, though they say dreadful things. They say rose windows in cathedrals are vaginal symbols.) Your legs, exposed as fully as by a bathing suit, yearn deeper into the amber wash of heat. Well: begin. A green jet of flame spits out sideways from a pocket of resin in a log, crying, and the orange shadows on the ceiling sway with fresh life. Begin.

"Remember, on our honeymoon, how the top of the kerosene heater made a great big rose window on the ceiling?"

"Vnn." Your chin goes to your knees, your shins draw in, all is retracted. Not much to remember, perhaps, for you; blood badly spilled, clumsiness of all sorts. "It was cold for June."

"Mommy, what was cold? What did you say?" the girl asks, enunciating angrily, determined not to let language slip on her tongue and tumble her so that we laugh.

"A house where Daddy and I stayed one time."

"I don't like dat," the boy says, and throws a half bun painted with chartreuse mustard onto the floor.

You pick it up and with beautiful sombre musing ask, "Isn't that funny? Did any of the others have mustard on them?"

"I *hate* dat," the boy insists; he is two. Language is to him thick vague handles swirling by; he grabs what he can.

"Here. He can have mine. Give me his." I pass my hamburger over, you take it, he takes it from you, there is nowhere a ripple of gratitude. There is no more praise of my heroism in fetching Sunday supper, saving you labor. Cunning, you sense, and sense that I sense your knowledge, that I had hoped to hoard your energy toward a more ecstatic spending. We sense everything between us, every ripple, existent and nonexistent; it is tiring. Courting a wife takes tenfold the strength of winning an ignorant girl. The fire shifts, shattering fragments of newspaper that carry in lighter gray the ghost of the ink of their message. You huddle your legs and bring the skirt back over them. With a sizzling noise like the sighs of the exhausted logs, the baby sucks the last from his bottle, drops it to the floor with its distasteful hoax of vacant suds, and begins to cry. His egotist's mouth opens; the delicate membrane of his satisfaction tears. You pick him up and stand. You love the baby more than me.

Who would have thought, blood once spilled, that no barrier would be broken, that you would be each time healed into a virgin again? Tall, fair, obscure, remote, and courteous.

We put the children to bed, one by one, in reverse order of birth. I am limitlessly patient, paternal, good. Yet you know. We watch the paper bags and cartons ignite on the breathing pillow of embers, read, watch television, eat crackers, it does not matter. Eleven comes. For a tingling moment you stand on the bedroom rug in your underpants, untangling your nightie; oh, fat white sweet fat fatness. In bed you read. About Richard Nixon. He fascinates you; you hate him. You know how he defeated Jerry Voorhis, martyred Mrs. Douglas, how he played poker in the Navy despite being a Quaker, every fiendish trick, every low adaptation. Oh my Lord. Let's let the poor man go to bed. We're none of us perfect. "Hey let's turn out the light."

"Wait. He's just about to get Hiss convicted. It's very strange. It says he acted honorably."

"I'm sure he did." I reach for the switch.

"No. Wait. Just till I finish this chapter. I'm sure there'll be something at the end."

"Honey, Hiss was guilty. We're all guilty. Conceived in con-cupiscence, we die unrepentant." Once my ornate words wooed you.

I lie against your filmy convex back. You read sideways, a sleepy trick. I see the page through the fringe of your hair, sharp and white as a wedge of crystal. Suddenly it slips. The book has slipped from your hand. You are asleep. Oh cunning trick, cun-ning. In the darkness I consider. Cunning. The headlights of cars accidentally slide fanning slits of light around our walls and ceiling. The great rose window was projected upward through the petal-shaped perforations in the top of the black kerosene stove, which we stood in the center of the floor. As the flame on the circular wick flickered, the wide soft star of interlocked penumbrae moved and waved as if it were printed on a silk cloth being gently tugged or slowly blown. Its color soft blurred blood. We pay dear in blood for our peaceful homes.

In the morning, to my relief, you are ugly. Monday's wan break-fast light bleaches you blotchily, drains the goodness from your thickness, makes the bathrobe a limp stained tube flapping dis-consolately, exposing sallow décolletage. The skin between your breasts a sad yellow. I feast with the coffee on your drabness. Every wrinkle and sickly tint a relief and a revenge. The children yammer. The toaster sticks. Seven years have worn this woman.

The man, he arrows off to work, jousting for right of way, veer-ing on the thin hard edge of the legal speed limit. Out of domestic muddle, softness, pallor, flaccidity: into the city. Stone is his province. The winning of coin. The maneuvering of abstractions. Making heartless things run. Oh the inanimate, adamant joys of job!

I return with my head enmeshed in a machine. A technicality it would take weeks to explain to you snags my brain; I fiddle with phrases and numbers all the blind evening. You serve me supper as a waitress—as less than a waitress, for I have known you. The children touch me timidly, as they would a steep girder bolted into a framework whose height they don't understand. They drift into sleep securely. We survive their passing in calm parallelity. My thoughts rework in chronic right angles the same snagging cir-cuits on the same professional grid. You rustle the book about

Nixon; vanish upstairs into the plumbing; the bathtub pipes cry. In my head I seem to have found the stuck switch at last: I push at it; it jams; I push; it is jammed. I grow dizzy, churning with cigarettes. I circle the room aimlessly.

So I am taken by surprise at a turning when at the meaningful hour of ten you come with a kiss of toothpaste to me moist and girlish and quick; the momentous moral of this story being, An expected gift is not worth giving.

*   *

Mommy says you don't love her any more.

HERBERT GOLD

from

LOVE AND LIKE

. . . PAULA, who was six, said to her father, "Mommy says you don't love her any more."

Her father, who was thirty-two, replied, "No, but I like her."

"But, but," said Cynthia, who was just four. "But can I go out and find Gary?"

"Why don't you stay with me for a little while?" her father asked. Dismayed by his querulousness, he repeated the remark in another voice. "Stay here with me. I have to go back soon. Anyway," he added, "it's almost bedtime."

"Okay," said Cynthia, resigned. She was a very small child, pouting and serious, with overbusy limbs. She paced back and forth on the long, low, especially constructed, "contemporary" couch which her mother had bought partly because her father didn't want it.

"But *why* don't you love Mommy any more?" Paula insisted. "You always told me you did."

"That was b-b-before." Her father stammered for an explanation, dulled by knowing that there could be no valid one for

Paula. "I tried—we did—I wanted to. We just weren't happy together. You know how that is, Paula."

"No," she said flatly and firmly.

"We have to live separately. It's like when you and Cynthia are tired and quarrel. We put you in separate rooms until you feel better."

"When are you and Mommy going to feel better?"

"It's not exactly that way with grownups." The sly innocence of Paula's question brought his hand out to touch her pleadingly; he wiped away the smudge of dirt on her cheek. She always made herself up with a stroke of dust as soon as possible when her mother washed her face. Cynthia, humming to herself, was listening with a smudge of prying watchfulness across her eyes. With a premature false security, the two girls frowned for serious discussion. The children of the divorced are engaged too soon in love as a strategy. Joy recedes before strategy; these children are robbed of their childhood. The huge brooding of possibility which human beings have at their best comes of the long passionate carnival of childhood; no fear of cost down this midway, just another and another breath-taking joyride on the great rollercoaster! and another quiet gathering-in of food and rest—it should be. It should be a storing of unquestioned certainties for the infinite risks of being a person. But instead, instead. Heavily Shaper touched the two girls as if to make them child animals again. It was not right that a father should feel this hopeless pity, and this need to enlist his daughters in the harried legions of rationality: "Here's how it is with grownups—"

"You mean Mommy and you?"

"Yes. Yes. Now listen. We feel better living in separate places. We're going to stay like that. But we like each other, Paula, and we love you and Cynthia. We both do."

"But, but, but, but," Cynthia sang, carefully wiping her feet on the pillows. "But heigh-ho, the derry-oh, the farmer takes a wife."

"Cynthia," said her father, "you shouldn't. Take off your shoes if you're going to play on the couch. It wasn't made for children."

Cynthia looked at him silently and, scraping the fabric, slid down beside him. Paula pulled between his knees, fighting to get closer than her sister. She began to suck her thumb. Her father pressed his lips together, resisted the temptation to remove her thumb from her mouth, and instead lit a cigarette. He decided that perhaps his silence would oblige her to remove the thumb and speak. It did not. At last he said, "I want you to understand. Mommy wants you to understand, too. Even though I'm not going to be Mommy's husband anymore, I'll always be your father. I couldn't change that even if I wanted to, and besides, I would never want to. Don't you want always to be my daughters?"

Sucking busily, Paula said nothing.

Cynthia announced with a grin, "But I want a daddy who loves my mommy. I think maybe Uncle Carl, he loves Mommy—" The look on her father's face told her that he was not enjoying her joke. "But I *know* you're my daddy for real."

"I am. For real."

"Okay," she said, bored with the discussion.

Paula looked at her wet and slippery thumb, considered putting it back, had another idea. "Why doesn't Mommy say hardly anything to you no more?"

"*Any* more," her father said. "I already explained. Because we don't get along—just like we don't let you and Cynthia talk to each other when you don't get along—"

"But we do anyway! But that's only for a few minutes! But it's not, not, *not* the same thing, Daddy!"

"No," he said, "you're right. It's really not."

"Then *when?*"

"When what?"

"When are you coming to sleep here again?"

"I told you, I already explained. Mommy and I—"

"When you went away you said you'd come back to live here in a few days."

"Well, we thought maybe. I hoped. But it's worked out this way instead. Now listen to me, girls, it's not really so different. I see you very often. We go out together for milk shakes. We're just like before."

Silence from Cynthia. From Paula, coldly, suddenly with her mother's precise articulation: "It's not the same, and you know it."

"Okay, you're right, it's not." Her recognition of his hollow heartiness made him flush. She cut right through what he said.

She remembered very well that he had been a part of the life of the house and she did not like her new sense of the house. He said, "I guess you're right, Paula, but that's how it is. That's all. We don't have to talk about it."

Silence. Then:

"So you really don't love Mommy any more." But she was a child again. The moment when she spoke with her mother's voice had passed. "Daddy," she said.

He resolved to go through it patiently once more. "No," he said, "and she doesn't love me. But we like each other, and we love and like you, both together, and we always will. You understand that, Cynthia?"

"Okay," said Cynthia.

Paula was sucking her thumb again. Her mouth was pulled around, working and bothering, as if she were trying to pull the skin off. She might be learning to bite the nail.

From the back of the house her mother walked toward the living room where the two children and their father were talking. She said hello, picked up a book, and returned to the bedroom. This meant that she would like him to notice that his time was up. A brisk, dark young woman, she was freshly showered and very pretty, although too thin. She wore a housecoat, but a girdle under it, stockings, and high-heeled shoes. Obviously she wanted to get the girls to bed early because she was going out.

He began to say goodbye to his daughters. He reminded them that he would come to see them at noon tomorrow. Cynthia threw her arms around his neck, laughing, and demanded: "Bring me something, maybe a surprise!"

"If you like," he said. He had a sick lonely weakness in his stomach of something not yet done, not possible.

"Do you like me, Daddy?"

"I like you and love you, Cynthia kid."

Paula was rubbing her face against his hand, the thumb still in her mouth. He lifted her to kiss her, saying, "And Paula too. Now goodbye until tomorrow."

As he started down the stairs, Paula stood with her swollen thumb dripping and shouted after him: "Oh how I'm sick of those words love and like!"

MORTAL

If your father's understanding fail, be considerate.

BEN SIRA. APOCRYPHA 3:13

AMBITION

All fathers entertain the pious wish of seeing their own lacks realized in their sons. It is quite as though one could live for a second time and put in full use all the experience of one's first career. . . .

JOHANN WOLFGANG VON GOETHE

BIRTHDAYS

The next person who takes a slingshot out of his pocket will be sent home at once. . . .

JOHN MASON BROWN
Happy Birthday

My WIFE had planned it carefully. Before that Saturday was over, we were to learn the afternoon was to take far more than careful planning.

"Movies in the front hall here?" I had asked, thinking back to those earlier birthday parties where, with a borrowed machine and six chairs of Baby Bear size, we had quieted the young until suppertime with rented films of Mickey Mouse and Felix the Cat.

"Dear me, no. At nine? They're much too old for that. He's asking them here for lunch, not supper this year. Eight of them. Then, I thought we'd take them to the Rodeo."

"The Rodeo?" I gasped, looking tired already.

"Of course. They'll love it. Besides, it'll get them out of the apartment."

I knew what she meant. Any parent would know. So would any house-owner who was not a professional wrecker. I remembered the growing damage of those earlier parties as gradually the puréed peas and scrambled eggs had given way to meat balls and peas unpuréed. Although less and less milk had been sloshed on the table, the noise and debris had swelled each year as the first conversational goo-goos had changed into the constant roar of simulated ack-ack. The wide-open spaces of Madison Square Garden were an inspiration.

"A wonderful idea," said I. "I'll get the tickets today."

They were asked for twelve-thirty. This meant, of course, that most of them came at twelve. The doorbell began ringing then with a violence grown-ups are unable to muster. They arrived when my wife and I, as exiles from the dining room, were still gobbling a quick lunch on trays in the living room.

Illness had taken a lighter toll than usual. Only one of the eight was missing. The others turned out to be either classmates in school or Park friends since the buggy-pushing days of long ago. Some of them wore short trousers under their blue jackets, some long—their first long pants. Although those so encased resembled pygmies seen through the wrong end of opera glasses, they felt superior. You sensed this the moment they appeared. They sported the happy look of the recently promoted. They were burdened by the same self-consciousness, too.

Three were deposited by their nurses; two by their mothers. "When can we expect him home?" each nurse or mother invariably demanded. "Not until five-thirty or so," my wife or I would say. Thereupon the faces of these women changed imperceptibly. A telltale suggestion of relief—or was it gratitude?—brightened their eyes. As a storm signal, this should have been warning enough.

The first fifteen minutes were occupied with the presentation and inspection of presents. Every time the bell rang, the birthday-boy would scamper down the hall, accompanied by his four-year-old brother. The latter, because of having been included in such venerable company, could not have been prouder had he met Eisenhower.

"Hi, Alfred!" "Hi, David!" Or "Hi, Harold!" the two boys

would call, with arms outstretched. Before any answers could be given, and the prepared speech regretfully made, the presents were snatched from the bestowing hand, and a race started to the nine-year-old's bedroom.

My wife and I stayed in the living room as a rather unwelcome welcoming committee. Everything seemed to be going satisfactorily back in his room, until the air was atomized by sudden shrieks.

"I wanna come in! I wanna come in!"

It was the little fellow's voice. He was bawling, his heart broken. After a few minutes I could stand neither his agony nor my own. Following Ford's example, I went on a peace mission.

"What's the matter?" I demanded, pushing past him and hard against a stoutly defended door. When the door at last gave way, I was confronted by a room filled with dropped wrapping paper, disordered ribbons, shiny toys, screams of delight, little boys, the rat-tat-tat of a machine gun, and the smells of a new chemistry set already in use.

"We told him he could stay out there and stand guard," said one of the bigger boys, amazed that anyone should not find joy in such an assignment.

"Let him in right this minute," said I, "and no more foolishness." Then I hastily retreated. Partly because I had just been hit in the face by a paper wad released from a slingshot. But mainly because I realized that my tones had been scarcely those which, as a host, I employed for adult guests.

A few minutes later his nurse appeared at the living room door. Already she had a tattered look. "Please come," she said; "they are shooting at people in the street."

I dashed back to find the window in his room open, and three of the little boys leaning out of it, peppering passers-by with their slingshots.

Once again, I'm afraid, my voice got out of control. "Put them down this instant," I ordered. To my astonishment I saw that even those who were not leaning out of the window had upraised slingshots in their hands.

"The next person who takes a slingshot out of his pocket will be sent home at once without lunch," I thundered charmingly.

The boys eyed me angrily but uncowed. "Without ice cream!"
I added. Two slingshots came down. "And he won't go to the
Rodeo at all!" Every slingshot slunk into a protecting pocket.

"Where's Richard?" I asked, trying to remind them that I
could be a considerate host.

"He's not here," the little boy muttered.

This time, when I left the room, a chorus of voices followed
me. "I tell you what, let's gang up on Richard."—"Say, that's
neat."—"When he comes, let's all get guns and hide in the front
hall and attack him."

At that moment the doorbell rang. And Richard appeared with
his mother. There was a brief armistice for company manners.
During it I could have sworn I saw small figures at the far end
of the hall creeping behind corners into imaginary pillboxes. They
proved to be wily strategists, these juvenile commandos. They
waited. A deceptive quiet settled on the apartment until Richard's mother left, and Richard started back with my sons, sup-
posedly to the older boy's bedroom. H-hour struck halfway down
the hall. An H-hour as much Comanche as it was Krupp.

"Stop it," I cried; "that's no way to treat Richard." But Richard
didn't seem to mind at all. As an invading force, he was letting
out a bombardment calculated to neutralize all shore defenses.

"I wonder when lunch will be ready," my wife asked. It was
the tenth time she had asked this same question during the past
quarter-hour.

"I was just about to ask you again," said I.

Finally, however, lunch was ready. After the inevitable last-
minute trips to the bathroom, they trooped into the dining room.

No party our friends had ever come to proved as noisily conversational as this one. Few bachelor dinners have ever so shaken
the chandeliers.

My wife and I appeared only at moments of climax, which
meant that we came in fairly often. Sudden summits of sound
gave us our entrance cues. These came whenever favors were
being hurled across the table, paper hats were being exchanged
without consent, or when two guests were delightedly spitting
in each other's faces. In comparison, the pop of snappers seemed
to us as gentle as a lullaby. Although there was a good deal of

simultaneous soliloquizing, there was little small talk. The conversation, when distinguishable from a barrage, consisted chiefly of fragrant descriptions of rival schools or discussions of figures in the comics utterly unknown to us. It ranged from sudden booms followed by "Say, listen to that atomic bomb!" to boastful inquiries as to how many times this or that boy had been to the Rodeo.

At last, after a good deal of coaxing and commanding, the main course was finished, and the ice cream served. Then came the great moment, the moment blissful and friendly, when the lighted cake flickered at the pantry door as the signal for cease firing and the singing of "Happy Birthday." When the wish was made, the candles blown out, and the cake sliced, one little boy screamed, "No cake for me. I hate it."

By then, the Wild West was calling. It was time to get going, which meant going to the bathroom once again on a community plan.

It's appalling how children can make scoutmasters of us all. My wife and I suddenly heard ourselves clapping our hands peremptorily and saying, without so much as a blush, "Now we will divide into teams. You're on my team, Harold. You're on my team, David."

When this sheep and goat separation was finally effected, and the right coats, caps, and gloves had been claimed by and put on the right boys, our two groups started for the elevator.

Just when its doors opened, one boy shoved another in play. He picked the wrong one. Every group of kids seems to include one who has taken boxing lessons. He functions like a tank among archers. The pushed boy had not put on his gloves in vain. He felt he had been exposed to a sneak attack. He retaliated in kind, waging war without declaring it in the best Japanese tradition. His right arm swung out, administering near the left eye of his friend a sock of which Cashel Byron would have been proud. The howls which followed were natural and instantaneous. So was the confusion. I found myself in the midst of the ring, a referee taking sides. I refused to admit the pugilist into my taxi. This meant another regrouping, and another slight delay.

When the two taxis were loaded, they proved noisier than

calliopes. I remember only two things about the ride down. One was vigorously applying my handkerchief to the running eye of the bruised boy. The other was the moment when the noise in the cab became so great that the driver stopped the car to say, "Listen, you kids, either shut up or get out!"

Upon reaching the Garden, our car emptied like the Trojan horse. The Rodeo, when seen alone, is wearing enough. When seen in the company of seven little boys, it is downright exhausting. You not only watch the bucking broncos; you are surrounded by them.

The performance in the ring that afternoon is blurred in my mind. I didn't get to see much of it. I spent most of my time in the men's room. I functioned more as a shepherd than as a spectator.

I soon reached the conclusion that Aristotle must have had a rodeo rather than a tragedy in mind when he spoke of the purgation of emotion through pity and fear. At least seven times during the afternoon I climbed over the people either behind me or around me, to lead little boys on private missions. Once I had all seven of them with me, including the four-year-old. By this time the others were completely at home on the range. He, however, was paying his first visit. Although there are pleasanter places than the men's room at the Garden, he thought it charming. No toreador could have been happier. With a look of excitement on his face he took a deep inhale, and said, so that everyone could hear him, "Oh, Daddy, smell the bulls!"

Even when not convoying the young, I could not give my full attention to the ring. For one thing, I never realized that people could ask so many questions, or such questions, in voices so loud. "What's a steer?" demanded one little fellow, while every adult head in the row in front of me turned around to await the answer.

Then, there were the vendors. Being astute psychologists, they sized up my predicament in a moment, and hovered around me like planes returning to a carrier. Popcorn, peanuts, spun candy, Coca-Cola, ice cream—these were simple enough; inexpensive, too. I didn't mind them. The real hazards were the men who came by screaming, "Want a cowboy belt?" "Want a Roy Rogers pistol?" "Want a Western whip?"

"Will you buy me one?" asked each little boy, in spite of the fact that the prices ranged from fifty cents to a dollar and a half.

"No!" I would say firmly. "No!"

"Oh, Daddy!" my nine-year-old would snarl, not only indignant but ashamed. And six other sneering faces would pivot towards me. From them I learned something I had never before suspected. A Bronx cheer can be silent.

Just before the time came to leave, I was cowardly enough to surrender. I began to wonder what these boys would say to their fathers about my son's father. Accordingly, I bought each boy at fifty cents apiece chameleons or turtles that I knew could be purchased for ten cents three blocks away.

The leaving was not without its difficulties. My wife and I desired to get out before the crowd. Our guests desired to stay until after the crowd had left. We won, however, although not without a struggle.

Then, once again, we divided into teams. Once again with our teams we crawled into separate taxis. Our last job was to deposit each boy at his respective doorstep.

When we got home, and our boy had had his supper, he said, his eyes still glistening, "Wasn't it a wonderful birthday!" Then he went to bed. So did we. At once.

CARS

A pedestrian is a man whose son is home from college.

UNKNOWN

DEFEAT

What are we going to say to him?

NATHANIEL BENCHLEY

from

A FIRM WORD OR TWO

GEORGE ADAMS held open the door of the school gymnasium for his wife, then followed her in. The smell of steam heat and liniment and disinfectant was the same as it had been twenty-five years before, and he could hear the scurrying, pounding feet of basketball players, punctuated by the sharp tweets of the referee's whistle. It never changes, Adams thought. Every smell and every sound is still the same. He led Eleanor past the basketball court, then through another door and up a short flight of steps to the gallery above the swimming pool.

The room was of white tile and glass brick, and it was steaming hot and echoed hollowly with a noise of its own. Adams and his wife sat down behind a railing overlooking the pool, and Adams took off his topcoat and put it on the seat beside him.

"I'm getting nervous already," Eleanor said. "Do you think they have a chance?"

"All I know is what Bobby—excuse me—Bob said," Adams replied. "He didn't seem to think so."

"I don't really care, so long as Bob wins his race," she said. "I think he'd die if he didn't win it, with you here, and all."

"He can't win it or not win it," said Adams. "He's in the two-hundred-yard relay, so there are three others with him."

"I know, but still . . ." Eleanor took off her coat, and peered down at the green, transparent water of the pool. "It looks awfully long, doesn't it?" she said.

Adams looked at the pool, and estimated that he could swim about one length—maybe two, if he took it easy. "Long enough," he said.

Two lanky, muscular figures wearing the bright-blue trunks of the rival school walked out of the door at one end of the pool and dived flatly into the water, hitting it with a double crack like pistol shots. Then more boys in blue trunks came out and followed them, until the whole squad was swimming up and down the length of the pool. At the diving board, two boys took turns doing unbelievably complicated dives, and Adams and his wife watched them with a kind of uneasy respect.

"It looks as though Bob were right," Adams said after a while. "They look pretty good."

"I know," said Eleanor. "Much too good."

Then Bob's team, wearing red trunks, appeared and dived into the water and swam up and down the pool. At first, Adams had trouble recognizing his son among the twisting, thrashing bodies. The boys all swam alike, with long, powerful strokes, and they made insane-looking, bottoms-up turns at either end of the pool, and Adams thought back on the summer, many years ago, when he had had some difficulty teaching Bobby—Bob—to swim. As long as Adams held him, he would splash and paddle gleefully, but the minute Adams took his hands away he would become panic-stricken and sink. It wasn't until children younger than he had begun to swim that Bobby, without any help from his father, took his first strokes. He's certainly improved since then, Adams thought. I had no idea he could swim this well. Even last summer, he wasn't swimming like this. Then Adams looked at the others, in the blue trunks, and they seemed to be swimming just a little better. I guess it always looks that way, he thought. The other guys always look frighteningly good, even if they aren't. But this time they *are* better—there's no getting around it.

When the warmup was over, the two teams retired, and the officials began arranging their lists and checking their watches. It was the final meet of the season, the letter meet, and the gallery was full of spectators, both students and adults. From below came the sounds of more spectators, who were standing or sitting along the edge of the pool beneath the gallery, and the whole place hummed and echoed and rang with noise. Adams removed his jacket, put it next to his topcoat, and loosened his tie. He fought down an urge to light a cigarette, and locked his hands together in his lap. Eleanor reached across and clutched them briefly, and her hand was cold and wet. He smiled at her. "It's no good worrying now," he said. "Bob's race isn't until the very last."

There was a patter of applause as the rival team, wearing blue sweat suits, filed out and took places on benches set in three rows at the shallow end of the pool. A moment later, the air was shattered with cheers and whistles as Bob's team, in red sweat suits, came out and sat beside them. Presently, two boys from each team peeled off their sweat suits and dived into the pool, then pulled themselves out, shook hands all around, and waited, nervously flapping their arms and wrists. Adams looked at his son, who was sitting on the back row of benches, staring straight ahead of him and chewing a thumbnail. I wish I hadn't come, Adams thought. I wish I'd made up some excuse to stay at home. He remembered a time when he was young and his father had come to watch him play football, and he had spent the entire, miserable game on the bench. Parents should stay away from athletic contests, he told himself. They ought to be barred by law. Bob continued to chew his thumbnail, and Adams felt sick.

A manager with a megaphone announced the first event, which was the fifty-yard free-style race, and gave the names of the contestants. The starter pointed a blank pistol upward and told the boys to take their marks. There was a complete silence as they stood in a row at the edge of the pool, gripping the rim with their toes. The starter said "Get set," and the boys crouched, their hands on a level with their feet. There was a pause. The pistol banged, and after what seemed to Adams like an unnaturally long wait the boys shot forward, cracked into the water, and churned off down the pool.

The crowd shouted and called and cheered and chanted, and the noise swelled to a roar as the swimmers reached the far end of the pool, made their frantic, ducking turns, and headed back for the finish line. They were almost indistinguishable in the boiling spray, but the two in the farthest lane, the ones in the blue trunks, pulled steadily ahead in the final yards, and finished first and second. Adams settled back in his seat.

"That makes the score eight to one already," he said to his wife. "This is going to be murder."

But Bob's team placed first and third in the next event, and first and second in the one after that, and somehow, unbelievably, they managed to gain a slight lead. It was never a big enough lead to be safe, and at one point the score was tied, and Adams saw and pitied the agony of the one boy in each event who failed to score. Some drooped forlornly in the gutter, some cried, and some had to be helped from the pool by consoling teammates, who said futile things to them and patted them on the bottom while they dragged themselves to the benches. As the final event came closer, Adams looked more often at his son, and it seemed to him that Bob was getting smaller and paler with each race. I wish to God he'd swum first, Adams thought. I wish it was all over, so he wouldn't have to wait like this. Even if he'd lost, I wish it was all over.

The diving took a long time, with each of the four contestants doing six dives, and the next-to-last event was the medley relay race, which Bob's team won, putting them ahead, 37–30. When the score was announced, Eleanor gave a little shout and grabbed him. "We've won!" she cried. "They can't possibly catch us now!"

"It looks that way," Adams replied with a certain amount of relief. "It certainly looks that way."

A student behind him touched his arm. "No, sir," he said. "They can still tie us. The last race counts seven points, and there's no score for second."

"Oh!" said Adams. "Damn!" he added, half to himself.

He saw Bob and his three teammates strip off their sweat suits, jump into the water, then climb out, shake hands, and stand around fluttering their hands and breathing deeply. The boys from the other school did the same, and they looked big and unnaturally husky. They didn't seem as nervous as the boys on Bob's team. The noise from the crowd was such that the manager had to shout three times for quiet before he could announce the event, and when Bob was announced as swimming third in the relay, Adams had an odd feeling at the sound of the name. Eleanor slid her hand into his. "I don't think I'm going to be able to watch," she said. "You tell me what happens."

The first two swimmers took their marks, and a tense silence hung until the crack of the gun. Then, as the swimmers leaped out at the water, the spectators came to their feet and shouted and cheered and stamped, and the noise grew and swelled until Adams couldn't hear his own voice.

The swimmers thrashed down the pool and then back, and the one in red trunks was slightly ahead as they touched the starting line and two more swimmers sprang out. Adams didn't watch the second boys; all he saw was Bob, who had moved up to the starting line, breathing in deep gulps, his eyes fixed glassily ahead of him. An official squatted beside Bob's feet, and Bob crouched lower and lower as his teammate in the pool approached him. The red-trunked boy was leading by about two yards when he reached the edge, and it seemed to Adams that Bob was in the air and in the water at almost the same instant. Then Adams' throat closed and he couldn't make a sound, but beside him Eleanor was screaming and pounding the rail, her voice all but lost in the growing pandemonium.

Bob finished his lap three or four yards ahead, but as the last two swimmers raced down and turned, the one in blue trunks began to gain. He closed the gap slowly, and the members of both teams crowded around the finish line, jumping and beckoning and bellowing, and then the red-trunked boy put on a final, frenzied spurt and held his lead to the finish line. Bob and his teammates spilled into the water, hugging one another and falling down and shouting, and the blue-trunked boy clung to the gutter, exhausted and miserable.

Adams sat back and looked at his wife. "Wow!" he said. And she laughed.

Down below, members of both teams clustered around the officials, and then, suddenly, the ones in blue leaped into the air and shouted, and Adams saw a boy in red trunks hit the water with his fist. There was some commotion, and a lot of noise from the crowd, and Adams was unable to hear distinctly what the manager said through the megaphone, but he caught the words "Thirty-seven to thirty-seven."

Unbelieving, he turned to a student in the crowd. "What happened?" Adams asked. "I couldn't hear."

"We were disqualified," the student answered sourly. "Adams jumped the gun."

For almost a full minute, neither Adams nor his wife said

anything. Then he put on his coat and helped her on with hers, and as they walked slowly down the stairs she took his arm. "What are we going to say to him?" she asked in a small voice. "What *can* we say?"

"I wish I knew," he replied. "I wish to God I knew."

They went out to the car, and stood beside it smoking while they waited for Bob to come out. Adams' mind was a jumble of things he wanted to say, but even as he thought of them they seemed inadequate, and he knew that none of them would do any good. He thought of going in and seeing Bob in the locker room, and then quickly decided against it. I guess it's best to wait out here, he thought. He'll come out when he wants to.

After what seemed like an hour, Bob came out of the gym and walked slowly toward them. His hair was wet and slicked back, and his eyes were red—possibly from the chlorine in the pool, Adams thought, knowing that that wasn't the reason. Without a word, Bob opened a door of the car and dropped into the back seat. Adams got in front, and, after a moment's hesitation, Eleanor got in back with Bob.

"Do you want to drive around for a while?" Adams asked as he started the engine.

"Whatever you say," Bob replied. "I don't care."

They drove through the streets of the town and then out into the bleak, snow-spotted country. For several minutes nobody spoke, and then Adams cleared his threat. "Would you like me to tell you something?" he asked.

"Sure," said Bob, without enthusiasm.

"When I was in school, I wanted to play baseball," Adams said. "More than anything else, I wanted to make the baseball team. The only trouble was I wasn't good enough. I got in a couple of games as a pinch-hitter, and once they let me play right field, but I dropped the only fly that came my way, and they yanked me out." He looked into the rear-view mirror and saw the incredulous expression on his wife's face. He continued. "The last game in my senior year—the letter game—we were behind four to three in the ninth inning. We had a man on third, and the coach sent me in to bunt down toward first. On the first ball pitched, I tried to bunt, and the ball hit my right thumb and broke it. Technically, I was eligible for a letter, but I never collected it. I couldn't look at any of the team again."

Bob laughed shortly. "I never heard about that," he said.

"I didn't tell many people," Adams replied, with another look into the rear-view mirror. "But what I'm getting at is that these things are horrible when they happen—you think you'll never live them down—but sooner or later it gets so you can bear to think of them again. It may take a long while, but eventually it happens."

Bob was quiet for a minute. "I guess I was just trying too hard," he said, at last.

"I know," Adams replied. "And I promise you, next year we won't come up here to watch."

Bob looked at his father in the mirror. "O.K.," he said, and smiled.

*   *

Other sons might fail. Ours never had.

BENTZ PLAGEMANN

from

FATHER TO THE MAN

IMPENDING DISASTER does not always draw the members of a family closer together. Sometimes it acts as a centrifugal force, to send them spinning, and when the letter came from Princeton, saying that Cam was in trouble there, with his work, Kate and I spun. The letter was from the office of the dean, and arrived shortly after Cam had gone back after his operation. He was very seriously behind, the letter said, and unless definite progress was made at once, it seemed unlikely that he would pass.

It was Kate's conviction that Cam should resign at once. In this way he would avert what seemed to be inevitable failure, and with a period of interim study, he might apply again, and start over from the beginning.

I did not agree.

Trouble brought out the worst in each of us, as it so often does in less than perfect beings. And Cam, that less than perfect son of less than perfect beings, now became again, subconsciously, perhaps, an extension of ourselves, as he had been when he was a child.

In our way of thinking he became this. It seems astonishing to me now, in retrospect, that we, who thought of ourselves as reasonably intelligent people, never thought for once of consulting Cam about what he thought he should do under the circumstances, or what, in his opinion, his course of action should be. No. We would decide. We had decided everything for him for so long that no alternative appeared to us. We would decide what he should do, and then we would let him know.

Everyone was, I think, demeaned in some way or another by this course of action, not least of all Cam, who, among the many ways he would be punished by failure was that of being reduced to vassalage again.

The letter suggested that we make an appointment to come to Princeton to discuss this, and this I did, by telephone, setting a time two days away.

Kate elected not to go. It was not alone disapproval of my action. There were times when she felt that women appeared at a disadvantage, and she was careful to avoid those. Some matters had to be left up to men, and she did not relish the idea of appearing as a pleading mother, in a position of vulnerability, in a stronghold of men. At least I think this is probably what she felt. At the time we were communicating in Esperanto, a language suited best to exchanges of opinion about the weather.

But I think we both still hoped. We hoped that it would turn out all right. We hoped, I suppose, that it was all a mistake, or an unpleasant dream, and that we would waken, and the clouds would be gone, and all would be sunny again. And I think we also felt that this failure, if failure it was to be, might be a punishment for our pride. Other sons might be in trouble. Ours never had. Other sons might be difficult, or lazy, or ungrateful for opportunity. Ours never had. Other sons might fail. Ours never had. And again, our reflections were self-directed reflections. Cam was a planet in our orbit. Disturbance for him upset our celestial system. We could not see it clearly.

I put on my gravest mood, and my gravest suit, and two days

later drove to Princeton. The serenity of the campus was now a reproach to me. It seemed not merely benign, but indifferent. It was not only a world to which I could never be admitted again, it was also a world from which Cam might be expelled, and every carefree student face was a reproach to me, and a reminder of threat.

The office of the dean was indifference compounded, with its busy staff, and its desks and its filing cabinets, and the impartial sunlight flooding in at the windows. The dean presented me with the woeful evidence on paper, helpfully synthesized by calculating machines, and Cam's importance, and my own, seemed diminished, in this office where we were surrounded by hundreds of other records, hundreds of other orbital systems, all part of a greater galaxy, in which we were scarcely visible to the naked eye.

And there was no advice for us. Any decision, if a decision was to be made, had to be made by us. Princeton had already taken its position. Many were called, but few were chosen, and the ranks of the elect closed quickly behind those who did not qualify.

But an appointment had been made for me with Cam's adviser, and now I went to see this man, reflecting on the curious circumstances in which parents sometimes find themselves, and wondering how anything which began with stolen kisses in the dark could possibly have brought me to this point of academic trepidation, where I found myself trying to catch a reflection of myself in the glass door of an office to determine if I looked respectable enough for my errand.

As for Cam's adviser, I found Cam's description of him as sort of a square more generous than my own immediate impression. Here was not a square, but a cube, or even an isosceles triangle. Time has taken from me the memory of his name, a merciful Freudian benefit, rendering my dislike more impersonal. But this nameless paragon among men had not one, but two, or possibly even three sons. I forget that, too. At any rate, one thing was clear. From his superior point of vantage, or accomplishment, it followed that he knew twice or three times as much as I did about bringing up a son, and it was his opinion, an opinion without qualification, that Cam should withdraw from Princeton, and sign up for his military service.

I could not see the point of this, nor the reason why. (Other sons had to withdraw from college and do their military service. Ours did not.)

"It will give him time to grow up," the adviser said.

I replied that I considered him to be sufficiently grown-up for his age. . . .

"Isn't it possible for him to be tutored in math?" I said. "Can't he cram for the exams?" After all, Cam hadn't failed yet. He was in trouble, but he was resourceful, and I had seen him squeak out of other tight spots before. Other sons might fail. Ours did not. Not that this referred to him, except indirectly. Pride sat with me in the chair.

The adviser leaned back in his swivel chair, stretched out his legs, and crossed his ankles, revealing an admirable pair of argyle socks, presumably knitted for him at the fireside by an adoring and dim-witted wife. Complacency shielded him like a cloak. It seemed impossible to me to imagine that he could not feel the radiations of my dislike for him, but, shielded as he was, perhaps the effects of it would not be apparent until later, like the result of fallout, when he would suddenly disintegrate from the effects of my contempt. If there were emanations from him, I was protected by the leaden suit of my stubbornness.

He was trying to tell me something. It didn't seem to be too easy. Perhaps the oracle wasn't accustomed to the sound of voices coming back at him.

"It's a long haul, you know," he said, staring up at the ceiling, with his hands folded behind his head. "Eight years of primary school. Four years of high school. Then college, added to that, right away. Some boys falter. They just get tired. They need a little breathing space in between."

"I thought you were concerned about his growing up," I said.

"Well, but that is in some ways the same thing," he said, looking across at me. "Some boys just can't take the freedom of academic life."

"But that couldn't apply to Cam," I said. "He's been away at school for years. He was at boarding school. He spent a year away from home at a school in England. He did all right then. It isn't as if he hadn't had to develop his own discipline. . . ."

"It's very different in college, though," the adviser said. "A boy doesn't have the same supervision. No one tells him when to study." I remembered that Kate had said something like that, almost exactly, but both of them could be wrong. And there was another factor. I brought it out a little gruffly, feeling rather ashamed of myself, I suppose, as if I were using unfair tactics.

"He's been ill, you know," I said. "He missed a good deal of time."

"I am aware of that," the adviser said. "It's another reason I feel he should withdraw. He didn't allow himself any margin for error, before he was ill. He just got by then, and now that he's behind, it would take a superhuman effort to catch up again."

"But it could be done?" I said.

"I don't say that it couldn't be done," he said. "You—and he —will have to make that decision. I'm just saying that if he were my son, I would get him to withdraw."

But he isn't your son, I said to myself.

"I'll speak to him," I said aloud. "If he wants to try to make it, with tutoring, could you arrange that?"

"I could," the adviser said, raising himself to a sitting position again, abruptly, as if to signify that the interview was over. "We can ask an instructor, or an advanced student, to do that."

I stood up. "I'll talk to him now," I said.

I did not relish the interview. Like most fathers and sons, we had always avoided man-to-man talks. There was attachment between us, and communication, and we often enjoyed the company of each other, but our deepest feelings we expressed in other ways than talk. In passing, so to speak, or laconically, or while doing something else, like putting up the summer screens. I suppose women find this hard to understand, and I have sometimes noticed a tendency with them to blame many of the small failures of life on what they think of as an avoidance of duty, or an incomprehensible reluctance to talk. "Now you go upstairs and talk to him!" is one of the most dread pronouncements in all American households. As any parent knows, little girls generally learn to talk earlier than little boys, and it may well be that little boys learn to talk at all only to communicate with (or defend themselves from) little girls. In business, men like best to talk in groups, in boards of directors, in committee, in meetings. In friendship, or in the love between father and son, they prefer to go hunting, or fishing, or to sit together at a ball game. There is some atavism here, I suppose. To talk is to open a door, to place one's self in a vulnerable position. In business you can be taken advantage of. In love you can be hurt. And possibly the most difficult of all oral communications is between father and son.

It works both ways, as it was apparent to me almost at once after leaving the office of the dean. As I started across the campus, I saw Cam. Cam saw me. And he hid.

I had not told him I was coming. The letter from Princeton had made it quite clear that he had also been informed of his precarious position, so it wouldn't take much imagination on his part to know why I was there. Yet it seemed to me a measure of the magnitude of our problem that we now took to hiding from each other. He had run out of a classroom with others, at the end of a class, and in the brief moment I saw him before he ducked behind a tree, the effect was not encouraging. He was wearing soiled, crumpled khakis, a rumpled button-down shirt open at the neck, and dirty sneakers. From what I could observe of the others, it seemed to be the uniform of the day, yet Cam, unlike most of the others, was unshaven. Now that he was grown, an untidy exterior generally indicated an untidy state of mind. It was not a good omen.

I walked on, pretending that I had not seen him, and that I had not seen that he had seen me. Furthermore, I never told him that I had seen him hide. I let go of a little of him that day, I suppose, maybe even a great big piece of him. I don't think I was aware of that at the time, but in looking back I believe I can say that, as a general rule, when your son takes to hiding from you, it is time to let him go. But not that day. I had other fish to fry, and I went on to prepare the griddle.

He was not yet in his rooms when I arrived there. Bert was there, but no one else. He greeted me politely. Bert was a little less agonizingly shy, a little more confident of himself. I felt quite certain that no such letter had reached his father as had reached me. He was preparing to leave, and he said, "Excuse me, sir," and he departed.

I was alone in the ruins. I am convinced that one of the secondary reasons young men marry is merely from a final, desperate desire to have someone pick up after them. I cannot imagine that they really like the shambles in which they live when they live alone, yet to live in any other way seems completely beyond their powers. The coffeepot had run over on the hearth. The mustard pot was still on the mantel. There were empty beer cans and soda bottles on the bar, and above it was the missing barroom nude, a huge, flyblown chromo with the generous proportions so admired by our grandfathers, and whose presence there, at this moment of impending disaster, at least held out the cheering promise that there would always be a grandson.

Clothes were everywhere, clean and soiled. Little remains of former repasts were crumpled in bits of wax paper and old paper napkins. Books and papers were everywhere. Records were everywhere, and beyond the open doors of the bedrooms the unmade beds spilled out on the floor.

I waited. I thought I could re-create in my mind what was happening to delay Cam. By being seen first on my way to his rooms, I had cut off access to a change of clothes, but not to the community bathroom, and he was undoubtedly in there now, shaving.

He was. In a moment the door opened, and he stood there, sheepish, pink in the cheeks, nicked around the jowls. His hair was damped down, his shirt tucked in. He didn't say anything. He didn't say, "Oh, hello!" or "What a surprise!" or "I didn't know you were here!" He could hide from me when he saw me, but he couldn't lie. He wasn't dishonest. He just stood there.

"Sit down," I said.

I could dimly sense in my preoccupation with my own preoccupation how formidable I must appear to be. We had, each in our own way, dressed for Princeton University, but Cam had dressed for his peers, while I had dressed for the hierarchy. Since I did not go into town to business, I was very seldom seen around the house before sundown in a business suit and tie, and the effect now was rather like the dramatic confrontation in *High Noon*. I had even found myself brushing my hair with both hands that morning, holding a hairbrush in each hand, an act I performed only in moments of gravest parental responsibility. I had picked out the most uncompromising chair in the room, the only armchair, and in my concern for Cam, which was possibly the least visible of all elements of the scene, and my dislike for this occasion, I heard myself sounding like a Victorian pater-familias.

"I have just come from a talk with your adviser," I said.

Cam sank down on the sofa. He seemed to sag with its springs. A supportive beer can, dislodged, rolled across the room.

"You seem to be in trouble," I said.

"I guess so," Cam said.

He rummaged for a battered package of cigarettes in his trouser pocket, and offered me one. I took it. It was the only act of mercy I could think of. Cam struck a match for both of us, and we smoked a moment in silence.

"It's your same old trouble, isn't it?" I said.

Cam said nothing.

"It isn't that you aren't intelligent," I said. "God knows you have brains enough to do this work." I heard irritation, impatience, anger, pressing at the back of my voice, and I tried to subdue them, but not too successfully.

"You're just careless in your habits," I said, getting up and beginning to pace back and forth in the room. "You don't check back in your work, and you don't study enough. You think you know it, and you think you'll get by."

Cam said nothing, but he looked so crushed, so miserable, so unable to meet my eyes, that I felt contrite, and stopped, and went back and sat down in my chair.

"That was a bad break, about your operation," I said after a moment. "But people are willing to make allowances for it. Don't you think you could pull yourself together, and work hard, and still make it "

Cam looked up at me, tentatively, but the door burst open at that moment, and it was Horse.

"Oh, hello, sir!" he said, adjusting his beaming, open-faced, boyish smile. "Excuse me, sir," he said. "I didn't know you were here."

He went out again, shutting the door behind him. But there was no sound of retreating footsteps outside, and from further sounds of advancing footsteps and halting and retreat, I gathered that he had planted himself outside the door to assure our privacy, like a guard posted at the door of the dungeon, while the hero is being tortured inside.

Our hero, meanwhile, had gone into further retreat. After his tentative glance, he looked away. He climbed down inside himself somewhere, and pulled in all the ladders, and shut the trap doors behind him. Mothers have problems, I am quite willing to acknowledge, but at least they are spared the revelation of just what happens after they have said, "Now you go upstairs and talk to him!" Kate hadn't urged me to come, it was true, and she hadn't come with me because she didn't approve of what I was doing, but here we were, trapped in our unspeakable dilemma, and I went speaking on, knowing it was all going wrong, but unable to stop.

"I spoke to your adviser about having someone tutor you in math," I said.

Cam said nothing.

"Don't you think that's a good idea?" I said.

Cam shrugged, helplessly. He reached over to stub out his cigarette in an ashtray, but it was so filled with old butts he had to push them around a bit before he could find the bottom.

"Say something!" I said.

"Uh . . ." said Cam.

He didn't look at me. He just sagged there, his hands between his knees. He looked so dejected that a curious metamorphosis began to take place in me. I began to feel almost cheerful.

"Oh, come on," I said. "It can't be as bad as all that. Now look," I said, sounding like a graduate of the Dale Carnegie Institute. "It's just information in a book. You just have to read it, and study it, and memorize it. Now is that too difficult? Surely you can do that. I know you can! Granted, you are behind. But I've seen you take hold before in a spot like this." I smiled, feeling it on my face.

Cam looked up at me, patiently, as if I were slightly demented. Which, no doubt, I was. He scratched the back of his head.

"You aren't a quitter," I said. "You never were. If you buckle down to this, I'm sure you can make it." We had an unspoken agreement in our house never to use expressions like "buckle down," but that had been in the days before I had to get up and put on a business suit and a tie at nine o'clock in the morning.

"Why don't you talk to your adviser, and tell him you want to give it a try with a tutor," I said.

Cam scratched the back of his head again, and looked at his fingernails.

"Okay," he said.

I stood up. "Good," I said. "I knew you would feel that way. You're going to make it. Everything is going to come out all right." I was positively beaming.

Cam stood up, too. His wrinkled trousers didn't stand up all the way with him, which gave him sort of a sprung look. He ran the palms of his hands up and down the sides of them, absently.

"I've got to go now," I said, holding out my hand. "I'm glad we had this talk. It clears the air. Everything is going to be all right."

Cam shook my hand, rather unconvincingly, and the false cheeriness of my voice echoed in the room with the scratchy sound of an old victrola record.

"Good-by, sir," said Horse at the door. "Take it easy on the turnpike!"

*   *

DRINK

Father, dear Father, come home with me now,
The clock in the belfry strikes one;
You said you were coming right home from the shop
As soon as your day's work was done;
Our fire has gone out, our house is all dark,
And Mother's been watching since tea,
With poor brother Benny so sick in her arms
And no one to help her but me.

HENRY CLAY WORK: Come Home, Father

FATHER'S DAY

Today is Father's Day. If Dad is lucky Mom will take over for him. Perhaps . . . he'll be excused from fixing formula, giving bottles, washing the dinner dishes, helping with homework, supervising the youngsters' baths, and getting them off to bed. Maybe . . . Mom and the children will take him out to dinner!

DOROTHY BARCLAY
from THE NEW YORK TIMES MAGAZINE

*   *

. . . a father brings to his son what his son brings to the world.

ADLAI E. STEVENSON

ADDRESS BEFORE THE
NATIONAL FATHER'S DAY COMMITTEE*

I HAVE COME HERE TODAY not so much to accept an award as to strike a much needed blow for fatherhood in America.

There was a time when father amounted to something in the United States. He was held with some esteem in the community; he had some authority in his own household; his views were sometimes taken seriously by his children; and even his wife paid heed to him from time to time.

In recent years, however, especially since World War II, father has come upon sorry times. He is the butt of the comic strips; he is the boob of the radio and TV serials; and the favorite stooge of all our professional comedians.

In short, life with father seems to have degenerated into a continuous sequence of disrespect or tolerance at best. It appears

---

* May 25, 1961.

that the poor fellow is unable to hang a picture or hit a nail without some mishap; no radio or clock will ever work again after he fixes it; he can't boil water or even barbecue a steak, at least not without burning it.

Every time the so-called head of the household attempts to assert himself or express his opinions, the whole family is convulsed with indulgent if not scornful laughter.

Personally, I think all this has gone far enough, and father certainly needs his Day! So all of us fathers should be grateful to you for contriving this brief hour of recognition. I am honored that you have chosen me, a father and a grandfather.

I do not think we would want father restored to his nineteenth-century role of absolute monarch, but, even though we don't want him to be the autocrat of the breakfast table, I think we might consider giving him at least a polite seat at the table.

After forty or fifty years of life, after hard experience in the world of affairs, after education both in college and in the school of hard knocks, and after sweating away at earning a living for the whole family, it is conceivable that father could have learned a thing or two, and the rest of the family could listen to him with profit once in a while for the honor of raising a plaintive voice on behalf of so many. We might even have some better-behaved children if they did listen to him now and then. But of course I except my own children. I have to—or I might not survive Father's Day!

In all candor, I cannot say that I know for sure just how seriously my own children listen to me, but, God bless them, they at least pretend they do.

So all things considered, I have this suggestion to offer: Instead of a Father's Day, maybe we should try a Father's Year for a change. In any case, whatever we call it, let's have a New Deal for Dad!

Now it has been said that paternity is a career imposed on you one fine morning without any inquiry as to your fitness for it. That is why there are so many fathers who have children but so few children who have fathers.

Is there truth or cynicism in this remark? A bit of both, I imagine, but far too much of the former for my taste.

It is an all too visible truth that fatherhood is no longer the sacred duty it was once held to be. There are, today, far too many absentee fathers, fathers in name only. Paradoxically, and this is an insight into the nature of contemporary society, they are, in many cases, men whose ability, sense of responsibility and moral integrity outside the home are of the first order.

Apologists for these errant progenitors (in most instances, offenders themselves) have called up a multitude of rationalizations in their defense—two world wars in less than half a century, the pressures of modern urban life, business before pleasure, country before self and other tired old saws.

What nonsense. There is absolutely no excuse for a parent to abdicate his most important duty—the proper raising of his children. No father should be allowed to get away with the cowardly logic which concludes that his only job in the family is to pay for the bacon.

His role is much more grandiose than that. If it is to be properly fulfilled, he should be, in his realm, a man of many faces —an artist, a philosopher, a statesman and, above all, a prolific dispenser of good sense and justice.

But it is vitally important, especially in the early years, that his children see in father a working model of the social order in which, not so many years hence, they will be expected to play a dynamic part.

How can we, the parents, hope to secure a just and rational society if we neglect the development of those very instruments, our children, most necessary for its implementation? What good does it do to conceive grand moral, social or political plans for a better world if the children who will have to live them out fail to see their importance?

I know there are utopians who believe that human progress is inevitable, a divine trajectory irreversible in its upward motion. Let me just point out to them that in the last few thousand years we have blazed what I consider to be a trail of questionable glory —from Abraham and Isaac to Dennis the Menace.

I fear that no logic, no optimism can controvert the irrefutable equation that a father brings to his son what his son brings to the world. For sure, leaders in the Soviet Union believe this. In Russia, children are barely out of diapers before the full attention of the stage is focused squarely upon them. They are prodded, led and coaxed through the intricate social, moral and political byways of the system into which they were born. By the time they reach maturity their values are crystallized and they know their duties as responsible Soviet citizens.

In a democracy—in America—the state does not presume to be the father of the man. That responsibility is left to our schools, our churches and, most of all, to our parents.

On the contrary, to our way of thinking, it is the individual who is destined to become the father of the state. And to succeed in his parenthood, he must himself be well trained.

In a very real sense, a father's relations with his children should be a microcosmic reflection of their relations with the society in which they live. Through his actions a father must teach his children the intrinsic meaning of the democratic concept—freedom with restraint and the nature of integrity.

Several years ago, at a "Father-and-Son Team of the Year" ceremony held by the National Father's Day Committee, the father was the first to speak and said:

I claim no credit for my son being what he is . . . people make their own intellectual and moral characters. If he was helped in making his by me . . . it was he who decided to accept the help. The decision in such matters is finally with ourselves. To say that responsibility begins at home should mean, I think, that it begins—and ends, too—in the individual. Sooner or later he must help himself. There are no alibis.

The son then spoke of his father:

He has been able to move me, to laughter and to tears, for as long as I can remember, both in public and in private—and that's of the greatest importance. For my father has been to me both a public and a private man.

But my experience has reminded me of something that he taught me—not consciously, I'm sure, but as an example. For the extraordinary thing about my father is that his public face and his private face have been the same. He has been the same man to the world as he has been to his family. And that is harder than it sounds.

It is the very definition of integrity, I suppose.

In modern society everyone faces in some degree the problem of making his public face the same as his private face.

How far any individual succeeds in this effort—which is indeed harder than it sounds—may be taken as a rough measure of "public ethics" for our time and place. Thus in an era of growing artificiality of tinsel and packaging and makeup, and "falsies" of mind and body, the highest compliment that can be paid to a public man is paradoxically that he is made of the same stuff all the way through, inside and out. The more public responsibility he carries, the more important it is to have a private face that can without embarrassment be displayed in public.

I hope no one asks my sons how I've performed in that respect.

FREEDOM

When I was a boy I used to do what my father wanted. Now I have to do what my boy wants. My problem is: When am I going to do what I want?

SAM LEVENSON

GRIEF

And the king was much moved, and went up to the chamber over the gate and wept; and as he went, thus he said: "O my son Absalom, my son, my son Absalom! would I had died for thee, O Absalom, my son, my son!"

II SAMUEL XIX

*   *

. . . I must now drag on myself. . . .

JOHANN WOLFGANG VON GOETHE
A Letter to His Friend Zelter*

Weimar, November 21, 1830

Nemo ante orbitum beatus is a proverb that figures in history, but that actually does not mean anything. If it were expressed with some exactness, it would run: "Expect trials till the end."

You have not lacked them, my good friend, nor have I, and it is as though fate were convinced that we are woven together not of nerves, veins, arteries, and other structures derived from them, but of wire.

Thank you ror your kind letter! After all, once I had to give you such a message of grief as the greeting of hospitality. So let the matter rest as it is.

What is really curious and important in this trial is that all the burdens which I hoped soon—indeed, with the coming year—to take off myself and transfer to one younger than myself, I must now drag on myself and that they have even grown heavier.

At this point, only the great idea of duty can keep us erect. I have no worry except to move physically in equilibrium; everything else comes of itself. The body must, the spirit wills, and he who has prescribed the necessary path to his will need not think much.

I won't go farther, but I reserve for myself to progress from this point on occasion. My most heartfelt, most grateful greetings to all so loyally sympathizing with me.

HEREDITY

Nearly every man is a firm believer in heredity until his son makes a fool of himself.

UNKNOWN

---

* Five days earlier Goethe had learned that his only son had died in Rome.

The worst misfortune that can happen to an ordinary man is to have an extraordinary father.

AUSTIN O'MALLEY

IGNORANCE

. . . My Father and Mother, *in their serene discipline of me, never argued with one another, never even differed; their wills seemed absolutely one. My Mother always deferred to my Father, and in his absence spoke of him to me, as if he were all-wise. I confused him in some sense with God; at all events I believed that my Father knew everything and saw everything. One morning in my sixth year, my Mother and I were alone in the morning-room, when my Father came in and announced some fact to us. I was standing on the rug, gazing at him, and when he made this state-ment, I remember turning quickly, in embarrassment, and looking into the fire. The shock to me was as that of a thunderbolt, for what my Father had said* was not true. *My Mother and I, who had been present at the trifling incident, were aware that it had not happened exactly as it had been reported to him. My Mother gently told him so, and he accepted the correction. Nothing could possibly have been more trifling to my parents, but to me it meant an epoch. Here was the appalling discovery, never suspected be-fore, that my Father was not as God, and did not know everything. The shock was not caused by any suspicion that he was not telling the truth, as it appeared to him, but by the awful proof that he was not, as I had supposed, omniscient.*

EDMUND GOSSE: from FATHER AND SON

*   *

The lease said about I and my fathers trip from the Bureau of Manhattan to our new home the soonest mended. In some way ether I or he got balled up on the grand concorpse and the next thing you know we was thretning to swoop down on Pittsfield. Are you lost Daddy I arsked tenderly. Shut up he explained.

    RING W. LARDNER, JR.: from THE YOUNG IMMIGRUNTS

*   *

When I was a boy of 14, my father was so ignorant I could hardly stand to have the old man around. But when I got to be 21, I was astounded at how much the old man had learned in seven years.

    SAMUEL CLEMENS

JEALOUSY

It is no new observation, I believe, that a lover in most cases has no rival so much to be feared as the father.

    CHARLES LAMB: from THE WEDDING

MONEY

    A father is a banker provided by Nature.

    FRENCH PROVERB

*   *

Back in 1880 when I was a child, I asked my father for a cent. He heard me gravely and then informed me just as gravely that it looked to him as if a Democratic President would be elected that fall, and it behooved every prudent man to exercise especial thrift. Therefore, he would be obliged to deny my request.

CALVIN COOLIDGE

✳   ✳

My hair stands on end at the costs and charges of these boys. Why was I ever a father! Why was my father ever a father!

CHARLES DICKENS

✳   ✳

. . . many possessions, if they do not make a man better, are at least expected to make his children happier; and this pathetic hope is behind many exertions.

GEORGE SANTAYANA

✳   ✳

*And all to leave what with
    his toil had won
To that unfeather'd two-legged thing, a son.*

JOHN DRYDEN: from ABSALOM AND ACHITOPHEL

✳   ✳

There was an old man of Nantucket
Who kept all his cash in a bucket;
*   But his daughter named Nan,*
*   Ran away with a man—*
And as for the bucket, Nantucket.

UNKNOWN

WITH CHILDREN
SUDDENLY GROWN

Now they hardly seem my own . . .

WILLIAM ROSE BENET: from DAUGHTERS

She sends him the Bill of her Milliner.

GEORGE MEREDITH
A Letter to His Daughter Marie

Box Hill, July 10, 1891

To Miss Marie Meredith.

> *She scarce has a word for her Papa.*
> *To tell how she carolled and sported O!*
> *So, with just, How d'ye do and Ta-ta,*
> *She runs from her pen to be courted O!*
>
> *To write were a foolish endeavour,*
> *But, to show that her humour is still in her,*
> *And flourishing fatter than ever,*
> *She sends him the*
> *Bill of her Milliner.*

*   *

If you want to make your own way . . . why do I hold you back?

HENRY GREGOR FELSEN
from

Letters to a Teen-age Son:
Welcome Aboard Your Shakedown Cruise

How does it happen? How do we begin life as devoted parent and child, and, after years of living together, trying to love and please each other, end up as hostile strangers?

What happens along the way? Why can't we get along nicely "any more"?

We grope for explanations like the survivors of a mysterious explosion, stunned as much by surprise as by the blast.

The answer is, I think, that we are getting along as normally and successfully as we ever did, and as nicely as is possible at this time in your life. There are good, honest reasons why havoc seems to break loose during adolescence.

What we call growing up would be understood better if we called it growing away, and growing toward. For it is the process of growing away from needing the care, protection, assistance, restraints, affection and companionship of your parents, and toward becoming your own, independent self.

This natural destiny of yours is not in dispute around this house. The whole purpose of my fathering is to enable you to get along without me.

If I am for you, why do I so often seem against you? If I want you to be independent, why do I try to rule you? If I want you to make your own decisions, why do I try to tell you what they should be? If I want you to make your own way in the world, why do I hold you back? Why is it, the closer you come to manhood, the more I seem to pick on you?

Let me put it this way:

When you were an infant, I probably was more anxious than you that you learn to stand alone. The moment you could stand alone, I was more fearful than you that you might fall. But once you could stand, you pushed my hand away if I tried to help you —yet you grabbed trustingly for my legs whenever you felt yourself toppling.

Later on I was pleased that you could walk and run, but appalled at the dangers into which your active legs carried you. You could see cars, but you were too young to comprehend traffic, or understand danger. I wanted you to run, yet I had to prohibit you from running into the street. Of course you were furious when I restrained you, and sometimes you ran into the street just to prove you could if *you* wanted to. But whenever you fell and hurt yourself, even while defying me, you wanted and expected me to come to your aid and comfort you. Later, you wanted to hold my hand when there was a street to cross, once you were able to understand the dangers of the street.

This urge to be independent of me when and how you choose, and to depend on me when and how you choose, is part of your natural process of outgrowing me. Our life has followed this same pattern from the simple problems of babyhood to the present complex physical and emotional problems of adolescence.

The way we stand now, I continue to rejoice at each new step you take toward maturity and independence, but I must also, over your protests, continue to steer you away from new dangers that you can often see, but cannot yet comprehend.

So there is nothing new about the basic nature of our oppositions and head-butting. What has changed has been the amount of conflict, the kind of issues involved and the way we feel about our encounters.

Our conflicts reach their peak when you become a teen-ager for the same reason that the white horses eat more than the black horses—there just happen to be more of them.

When you were a little boy our conflicts—if we can even call them that—were brief, isolated, infrequent little skirmishes having to do with the simple little problems of your babyhood. Days, perhaps weeks would pass without a really cross word between us. We had more good times together than we had bad, yet it would be wrong to say that we got along better than we do now. It was your small size that limited the number of ways and times in which it was possible for us to battle.

Now that you are a teen-ager, we seem to be in conflict much of the time, and over everything. Naturally! The fact that you are, for the first time in our lives, my physical, mental and emotional equal, enables us to meet on all fronts with all forces.

Now that you are a man in every way, except that you are still a boy, the freedoms you seek are a man's, even though your methods of achieving them are often those of a child.

Your need is not merely to stand alone, or walk across the street alone, but to think alone, plan alone, dream alone, experience alone, achieve alone, suffer alone and become your mature self alone.

Just as you once had to walk alone on trembling legs to prove

that you were a little boy and not a baby, the time has come for
you to prove—in proving yourself a young man and not a boy—
that you can be intellectually and emotionally independent of me.
But though you flee my advice and brush away my affection, you
still need me close—*but hands off*—in case you begin to topple.

The fact that this growing-away process is natural does not
mean, as we are likely to assume, that it is easy. Nothing is more
natural than reproduction, yet the time of birth, the actual period
of transition from fetus to baby, is a time of pain and peril as
well as joy. And hardly less violent and hazardous, in its own way,
is the "natural" transition one makes from girl to woman, or from
boy to man.

It is what we are that creates the conflicts between us. It is who
we are that decides how we behave.

You know, when a new ship is built, it always goes through
a series of shakedown cruises before it is assigned to active,
equal duty with the fleet. The ship is taken out to sea and run
through every possible beam-wracking and engine-cracking maneuver. Emergencies of every kind are simulated, and every effort
is made to discover, before the ship is committed to action, all
flaws in the construction and handling of the ship, and in the
ability of the commander and crew.

I suppose adolescence could be described as the time of our
human shakedown cruises. A time when we shove off in an un-
tried ship manned by a green crew to make short, violent practice
runs in the safety of our home waters.

You are engaged in your final series of shakedown runs. This
is your last chance to practice, without serious risk, being independent and grown-up. It is your last chance to claim, simultane-
ously, the privileges of an adult and the responsibilities of a child.
It is your last chance to be a man in every way possible for a boy to
be.

One of the things that makes us so miserable now is that our
fights no longer seem to be waged over what you do, but over
what you are. Although I say I criticize your actions, what I seem
to dislike is you. When you buck my authority, what you seem
to reject is me as your father.

This too is a phase of the normal shakedown cruise.

In your necessary effort to test your ship, you must simulate every emergency, including that of being an orphan. In order to prove your ability to stay afloat alone if you had to, you must prove you can survive now without the parental love, approval, direction and protection that has been essential to your survival until now.

This accounts for the different nature of our conflicts. No longer are you merely testing the extent of my authority as your father. What is under attack now is the relationship itself. The only way to practice getting along without parents is to pretend they don't exist. The only way to find out how to live without love and approval is to reject them, and fight them off.

This explains—in part—why it is sometimes impossible to please, satisfy or love you; why you are hostile in response to affection, disobedient to orders, scornful of concern and at odds with the family's way of life. It helps explain why you sometimes seclude yourself physically, mentally and emotionally from the family, yet cling to home.

It used to irritate me to see you reject my love, sneer at my ideals, scoff at my counsel, oppose my wishes—yet make all kinds of extravagant demands on me for service and purchases. I did not understand that the shakedown cruise often tests a few selected areas at a time.

When it was time for you to reject my love and friendship, it was also necessary to demand more money, more things, more favors, more "proof" that I loved you during the test. And I have noticed that when you want to stand on your own feet economically, and make very few "things" requests of me, you are your most affectionate and companionable with me.

This need to prove your seaworthiness by fighting with me and rejecting me is transient, but it is not a game. Unless the emotions are real, the test is worthless. Honest heartache and genuine tears are the price we pay for your ticket to manhood. But it is a small price compared to what we would have to pay for peace during adolescence—your future manhood itself.

*   *

I writ to you a letter this day seven-night,
but never had any answer. . . .

EDMUND VERNEY
Two Letters to His Son Edmund*

London, 22 January, 1685

CHILD,

I shall be very joyful to hear of your safe arrival at Oxford, according to my kind wishes which attended you all the way for your pros-
perous journey.

I have this day sent you (by Thomas Moore the Oxon carrier) all
your things mentioned in this enclosed note, except your old camelot
coat, which I did not think you would need nor worth sending; your
old hat I did not send neither, for it is so bad that I was ashamed of
it. All your new things I bought you I put into a new box locked up
and well corded up, and the key of this box I have also here-enclosed
for you. But for the key of your trunk I could not find it, and it's no
matter, for that lock is nothing worth, and Tom made a shift to lock
it with a key of mine, and it is well corded besides.

In your old breeches which are in your new box, you will find your
five laced bands (the sixth you carried with you) and a new pair of
laced cuffs, and your two guineas in your fob, and a new knife and
fork in your great pocket. And so God bless you, and send you well
to do.

I am your loving father,
Edmund Verney

In your trunk I have put for you
   18 Seville oranges
    6 Malaga lemons
    3 pounds of brown sugar
    1 pound of white powdered sugar made up in quarters
    1 lb of brown sugar candy
    ¼ of a lb of white sugar candy
    1 lb of picked raisins, good for a cough
    4 nutmegs

---

* Because political upheaval in England had sent his father into exile, Edmund Verney was unable to attend college. However, he made certain his son
Edmund had the opportunity he was denied. These letters, as common today
as perhaps they were when they were written, were dispatched soon after young
Verney arrived at Oxford.

29 January, 1685

CHILD,

Mr. Palmer had a letter from his son at Oxford last Saturday morning very early, and my cousin Denton Nicholas wrote to his parents from Wycombe and again from Oxford since his last arrival. And when I take a journey I always write unto my father by every opportunity a perfect diurnal of my voyage and what else occurs worthy of remark. I writ to you a letter this day seven-night when I sent your trunk and box, but never had any answer nor account from you since, which is such a piece of omission in you, to say no worse, that I believe neither Oxford nor Cambridge can parallel. For why I should be thus neglected by my son I cannot imagine: indeed I look upon it as an ill omen, that you should commit such a gross solecism at your first entrance into the University against your loving father.

*   *

He was no puritan, he believed in young people enjoying themselves.

PHILIP ROTH

from

EPSTEIN

MICHAEL, the weekend guest, was to spend the night in one of the twin beds in Herbie's old room, where the baseball pictures still hung on the wall. Lou Epstein lay with his wife in the room with the bed pushed cater-corner. His daughter Sheila's bedroom was empty; she was at a meeting with her fiancé, the folk singer. In the corner of her room a childhood teddy bear balanced on its bottom, a VOTE SOCIALIST button pinned to its left ear; on her bookshelves, where volumes of Louisa May Alcott once gathered dust, were now collected the works of Howard Fast. The house was quiet. The only light burning was downstairs in the dining room where the *shabus* candles flickered in their tall golden holders and Herbie's *jahrzeit* candle trembled in its glass.

Epstein looked at the dark ceiling of his bedroom and let his head that had been bang-banging all day go blank for a moment. His wife Goldie breathed thickly beside him, as though she suffered from eternal bronchitis. Ten minutes before she had undressed and he had watched as she dropped her white nightdress over her head, over the breasts which had funneled down to her middle, over the behind like a bellows, the thighs and calves veined blue like a roadmap. What once could be pinched, what once was small and tight, now could be poked and pulled. Everything hung. He had shut his eyes while she had dressed for sleep and had tried to remember the Goldie of 1927, the Lou Epstein of 1927. Now he rolled his stomach against her backside, remembering, and reached around to hold her breasts. The nipples were dragged down like a cow's, long as his little finger. He rolled back to his own side.

A key turned in the front door—there was whispering, then the door gently shut. He tensed and waited for the noises—it didn't take those Socialists long. At night the noise from the zipping and the unzipping was enough to keep a man awake. "What are they doing down there?" he had screamed at his wife one Friday night, "trying on clothes?" Now, once again, he waited. It wasn't that he was against their playing. He was no puritan, he believed in young people enjoying themselves. Hadn't he been a young man himself? But in 1927 he and his wife were handsome people. Lou Epstein had never resembled that chinless, lazy smart aleck whose living was earned singing folk songs in a saloon, and who once had asked Epstein if it hadn't been "thrilling" to have lived through "a period of great social upheaval" like the thirties.

And his daughter, why couldn't she have grown up to be like —like the girl across the street whom Michael had the date with, the one whose father had died. Now there was a pretty girl. But not his Sheila. What happened, he wondered, what happened to that little pink-skinned baby? What year, what month did those skinny ankles grow thick as logs, the peaches-and-cream turn to pimples? That lovely child was now a twenty-three-year-old woman with "a social conscience"! Some conscience, he thought. She hunts all day for a picket line to march in so that at night she can come home and eat like a horse. . . . For her and that guitar plucker to touch each other's unmentionables seemed worse than sinful—it was disgusting. When Epstein tossed in bed and heard their panting and the zipping it sounded in his ears like thunder. Zip!

They were at it. He would ignore them, think of his other problems. The business . . . here he was a year away from the retirement he had planned but with no heir to Epstein Paper Bag Company. He had built the business from the ground, suffered and bled during the Depression and Roosevelt, only finally, with the war and Eisenhower to see it succeed. The thought of a stranger taking it over made him sick. But what could be done? Herbie, who would have been twenty-eight, had died of polio, age eleven. And Sheila, his last hope, had chosen as her intended a lazy man. What could he do? Does a man of fifty-nine all of a sudden start producing heirs?

Zip! Pant-pant-pant! Ahh!

He shut his ears and mind, tighter. He tried to recollect things and drown himself in them. For instance, dinner. . . .

*   *

I am prepared to be the young lady's slave. . . .

THOMAS HENRY HUXLEY

from

A LETTER TO HIS SON HENRY*

Eastbourne, Jan 30, 1890

YOU DEAR OLD HUMBUG OF A BOY—

Here we have been mourning over the relapses of influenza, which alone, as we said, could have torn you from your duties, and all the while it was nothing but an attack of palpitation such as young people are liable to and seem none of the worse for after all. We are as happy that you are happy as you can be yourself, though from your letter that seems to be saying a great deal. I am prepared to be the young lady's slave; pray tell her that I am a model father-in-law, with my

---

* The English biologist Thomas Huxley abandoned his own research to become in his country the leading advocate of Darwin's theories of evolution.

love. (By the way, you might mention her name; it is a miserable
detail, I know, but would be interesting.) . . . Ever your loving dad.

T. H. Huxley

*   *

What does she see *in him?*

BOOTH TARKINGTON

from

WOMEN

. . . LATE IN THE AFTERNOON Lily consented to take a little beef
tea and toast in her room; but she was still uttering intermittent
gurgles, like sobs too exhausted for a fuller expression, when her
mother brought her tray to her—or perhaps Lily merely renewed
the utterance of these sounds at sight of her mother—and all in
all the latter had what she called "a day indeed of it!"

So she told Mr. Dodge upon his arrival from his office that
evening. "*Haven't* I, though!" she added, and gave him so vivid
an account that, although he was tired, he got up from his easy
chair and paced the floor.

"It comes back to the same old, everlasting question," he said,
when she had concluded. "What does she *see* in him? What on
earth makes her act like that over this moron? There's the question I don't believe anybody can answer. She's always been a
fanciful, imaginative girl, but until this thing came over her she
appeared to be fairly close to normal. Of course, I supposed she'd
fall in love some day, but I thought she'd have a few remnants
of reason left when she did. I've heard of girls that acted like this,
but not many; and I never dreamed ours would be one of that
sort. I'd like to know what other parents have done who've had
daughters get into this state over some absolutely worthless cub
like Crabbe Osborne."

"I don't know," Mrs. Dodge said, helplessly. "I'd ask 'em if I
did. I'm sure I'm at my wits' end about it."

"We both are. I admit I haven't the faintest idea how to do anything more intelligent than we've been doing—and yet I see where it's going to end."

"Where, Roger? Where do you think it's going to end?"

"They've tried twice now," he said, gloomily. "Last time, if the idiot had taken the precaution to see that there was plenty of gas in his borrowed car before they started, they'd have been married. Some day before long he'll borrow *enough* gas, and then she's going to slip out and meet him again, and they will."

"No, no!" his wife protested. "I can't bear to hear you say so."

"It'll happen, just the same," he assured her, grimly. "Nothing on earth that we've done has been able to make her see this cub except as an angel—a persecuted angel. She really meant it when she called him that;—on my soul, I believe she did! We've told her the truth about him over and over till the repetition makes us sick. What effect does it have on her? We've told her what his own father said about him, that he's 'absolutely no good on earth and never will be!' What help was that? Then we tried having other people tell her their opinions of Crabbe. It only made her hate the other people. We've tried indulgence; we made the greatest effort to interest her in other things; we've tried to get her interested in other young men; we've tried giving her anything she wanted; we've tried to get her to travel; offered her Europe, Asia, and the whole globe; and then when she wouldn't go and everything else we tried was no good, we tried taking the whole thing as a joke—making good-natured fun of this cub; trying to make her see him as ridiculous—and the end of that was her first attempt to run away with him! Well, she did it again, and if we keep on as we're going she'll do it *again!* What's our alternative? I ask you!"

His wife could only moan that she didn't know;—her mind as well as her emotion was exhausted, she said; and the only thing she could suggest now was that he should try to get Lily to come down to dinner. He assented gloomily, "Well, I'll see, though it makes me sick to listen to her when she's like this," and went upstairs to his daughter's room.

After he had knocked repeatedly upon the door, obtaining only the significant response of silence, he turned the knob, found himself admitted into darkness, and pressed a button upon the wall just inside the door. The light, magically instantaneous, glowed from the apricot-coloured silk shades of two little lamps on slender tables, one at each side of the daintily painted bed; —and upon the soft green coverlet, with her fair and delicate head upon the lace pillow, lay his daughter. With hands pressed palm to palm upon her breast, her attitude was that of a crusader's lady in stone upon a tomb; and the closed eyes, the exquisite white profile, thin with suffering, the slender, long outline of her figure, could not fail to touch a father's heart. For the wasting of long-drawn anguish was truly sculptured there, even though the attitude might have been a little calculated.

"Lily," he said, gently, as he approached the bed, "your mother wants to know if you wouldn't like to come down to dinner."

The dark eyelids remained as they were; but the pale lips just moved. "No, thank you."

"You won't?"

"No."

"Then shall we send your dinner up to you, Lily?"

"No, thank you," she whispered.

He had come into the room testily, in a gloomy impatience; but she seemed so genuinely in pain and so pathetically fragile a contestant against her solid mother and against his own robust solidity that suddenly he lost every wish to chide her, even every wish to instruct her. He became weak with compassion, and the only wish left in him was the wish to make her happier. He sat down upon a painted little chair beside the bed.

"Lily, child," he said huskily, "for pity's sake, what is it you want?"

And again the pathetic lips just moved.

"You know, Papa."

There was something in the whispered word "Papa" that cried to him of sweetness under torture, and cried of it with so keen a sound that he groaned aloud. "O, baby girl!" he said, succumbing then and there, when he had least expected such a thing to happen to him. "We *can't* let you suffer like this! Don't you know we'll do anything on earth to make you happy?"

"No. You wouldn't do the one thing—Papa?"

"I said anything," he groaned.

. . . he was distinctly nervous.

EDWARD STREETER

from

FATHER OF THE BRIDE

THE DAY BEFORE the wedding came at last.

When one concentrates fiercely and at length on an event in the distant future it eventually becomes fixed in the mind as something forever remote. As a result it is a shock to awake some morning and find that the distant future has suddenly become the immediate present. It is like a foolish rumor about a lion in the district, which no one takes seriously until the beast springs at you from behind a lilac bush.

The wedding rehearsal was scheduled for five-thirty. Mr. Banks set out for the office exhibiting a nonchalance that he did not feel. Yes, of course, he would take the three-ten from town. There was nothing to get so excited about. Beneath the surface, however, he was distinctly nervous. He felt like a man moving beneath powerful floodlights.

The floodlight operator must have been off duty during his trip to town, however. The same apathetic faces greeted him at the station with the same apathetic comments about the weather, their health, or their lack of it. As the train pulled out of Fairview Manor, Reggie Fry lurched into the seat beside him and spent three stations describing an intricate real-estate deal in the course of which he had outwitted and discomfited the best brains in the business. Mr. Banks could stand it no longer.

"My daughter's getting married tomorrow," he said simply.

"Really?" said Mr. Fry. "Didn't know you had a daughter. Time flies, eh? I hope she's got a place to live after she's married. It's a bad situation. Getting worse. The Real-Estate Board put out some interesting figures about it in their last bulletin. I've got it here somewhere. Here it is. Now just let me read you these few paragraphs. This is on the volume of building of one-family homes in the mid-continent states during the first quarter."

Mr. Banks shuddered and gave himself up to his thoughts.

He would have found it hard to describe just what he expected when he arrived at the office. Obviously he had not anticipated organized cheering as he came in the door, yet it depressed him to have Miss Rooney nod to him from the switchboard and say, "MorningMrBanksnicemorning," just as she did on the other three hundred working days of the year.

Even his partners failed to grasp the significance of current events. As each one drifted into Mr. Banks' office during the morning he offered some fatuous remark about not falling down in the aisle or trying to bend over in his cutaway. Then, having made their concessions to the trivia of life, they concentrated on the task of dumping on his desk every unanswerable and boring problem they could dig out of their pending files. They reminded Mr. Banks of executives cleaning out their desks before leaving for their summer vacations.

During the moments when his partners were not bedeviling him the outside world took up the torch. The cream of the dullest and most long-winded of Mr. Banks' clients flocked into his office for no other apparent reason than to make sheep eyes at him and fill up an idle hour with the sound of their own voices.

The only positive note was the telephone. Whenever Mr. Banks thought about that morning during later years it was his telephone buzzer which sounded the motif of the nightmare cacophony.

"Darling, the worst thing. Old Mr. McQuade is down at the station.—McQuade, dear. *I* don't know. He's some relative of *yours.*—Well, it's no use arguing about that *now.* He's down at the station and he wants to know where he's supposed to *go.* Where in the world am I going to put him?"

Only the presence of a customer mooning beside his desk restrained Mr. Banks from detailed instructions.

"Hello. Is this you, Stanley?—This is Ella. *Ella.*—Is this Stanley Banks?—This is *Ella.* Yes. How *are* you? We came down the last minute as a surprise. Now we don't want you to bother your *head* about us. Just tell us how the trains run to Fairview Manor and how to get from the station to your house. If you haven't room to put us up we can go *anywhere* at all. The last thing we want to do is put you to any trouble. I guess you've got troubles enough just now." (Hysterical laughter.)

The sheep-eyed gentleman beside Mr. Banks' desk looked at him anxiously. "I hope that wasn't bad news," he said.

"No, no," said Mr. Banks. "I've got a daughter getting married tomorrow."

"Oh, of course. Quite," said the sheep-eyed gentleman and resumed his narrative.

"Darling, I'm so sorry to bother you again but I'm almost crazy. You can't imagine what's happened. The Bennett boy has come down with measles and they can't take in Cousin Laura and Bob. What in the *world* are we—I know, dear, but I thought you might have some *ideas.*"

By twelve-thirty he could stand it no longer. Shoving a pile of papers into a desk drawer, he rang for Miss Bellamy. "I'm getting the hell out of here," he said defiantly. The phone rang. "I'm gone."

"So sorry," murmured Miss Bellamy into the mouthpiece. "He was called away very hurriedly. He just this moment left the office. No, I don't think I could catch him. I know how sorry he'll be. He wanted to talk to you. Yes, I'll certainly tell him." She hung up the receiver. "It's that Mr. Wadley you've been trying to get for three days."

"That fellow has no judgment," said Mr. Banks.

"Yes indeed," said Miss Bellamy soothingly. "Now I have everything ready in this envelope. Here's a list of all the ushers and bridesmaids and where they're staying and their telephone numbers. And then here's a full set of church seating lists. There's one for each usher with his name typed on it and special instructions for those who have special jobs. I've put in some extra copies just in case. Oh, yes, and I've phoned all the papers just to make sure they remember and—well—I guess that's all till I see you in church."

Miss Bellamy looked suddenly deflated and wistful. Mr. Banks had never seen her like that before. For one terrible moment he thought she was going to cry.

"You've been wonderful," he said awkwardly. "Wonderful. I'll never forget it." He left quickly as the phone started to ring.

Several days earlier Miss Bellamy had sent crisp little notes to all the ushers and bridesmaids, attempting to impress upon their scattered minds that the rehearsal would be at five-thirty at St. George's Church and the importance of being prompt.

Mr. Banks had insisted on being there fifteen minutes ahead of time. He wanted this wedding well rehearsed—no sloppy business—and he felt somehow that if he and Mrs. Banks were early it would expedite things. To his dismay he found the church in complete darkness. The Reverend Mr. Galsworthy and the organist were nowhere about. The smoothly functioning machinery of St. George's was at dead center and the self-starter was missing.

Mr. Banks had pictured the organist busily warming up his instrument with a burst of arpeggios and Mr. Galsworthy nervously pacing the aisle, measuring distances, putting markers in his book and making a few final notes. Not even Mr. Tringle, the sexton, was puttering around.

He finally located Mr. Tringle in the cellar of the rectory gluing the back of a broken chair. "Good gracious," he exclaimed. "That late a'ready? Maybe we best go up an' put on the lights."

The first bridesmaid turned up at a quarter to six. She was a wispy little number who seemed to have been left out of everything to date and was obviously terrified at the thought of what lay ahead. The organist strolled in several minutes later.

"Are you sure," asked Mrs. Banks anxiously, "that you know what you are going to play at the wedding?"

"Oh, yes," said the organist. He was an earnest-looking young man with heavy horn spectacles. "Oh, quite. This is the Broadhurst wedding, isn't it?"

The knuckles of Mr. Banks' hand grew white as he clutched the end of the pew. "No," he said gently. "This is the *Banks* wedding —and it's *tomorrow*," he added with subtle sarcasm.

"Surely," agreed the organist and disappeared through the gloom of the side aisle.

By six-thirty Kay and all but four of the bridal party had appeared. The minister was still absent. The groom was still absent. The ushers and bridesmaids who had made the great sacrifice stood in small groups glaring at Mr. Banks with unconcealed hostility. It was evident that each and all had torn themselves away from agreeable situations for what they clearly considered to be an old-fashioned whim of Mr. Banks'. By their attitude they said, "You got us here. You ruined our fun. Now what are you going to do about it?"

It made Mr. Banks nervous. He distributed the seating lists to the ushers and made a little talk about over-all strategy. Somehow it didn't go very well. They listened to him with the detached boredom of tourists harangued by a Grand Canyon guide. Their aspirations were obviously elsewhere.

"I wonder where Mr. Galsworthy is?" asked Mr. Banks for the tenth time.

"Oh, he's somewhere. He's always late," said Mr. Tringle amiably. "I run the rehearsal."

"But some of the bridal party aren't here yet," protested Mr. Banks. "The groom isn't here. Nobody's here."

"Some of the bridal party is never here," said Mr. Tringle. "The groom don't do nothing in weddings. Everything goes all right. You see. Don't worry. Now if you young ladies will line up in pairs outside that there door—"

They lined up, tittering and unwilling, as people line up for a group photograph which nobody wants taken. Once in place they unlined immediately. Mr. Tringle pushed them back like errant cattle. "O.K., Fritz," he yelled irreligiously. The organ suddenly gave a series of bumps and broke into the wedding march. Mrs. Banks watched nervously from a pew.

"It's too fast," she cried hopelessly as the skeleton procession dashed past her "You're running. It's awful."

"You want to do it again?" asked Mr. Tringle, rubbing his hands with the air of one who has staged a great dramatic spectacle. "It comes O.K. next time. Take it easy. Line up now. Hey, you. Big girl. You get in back row this time so's they can see the other bridesmaids. O.K., Fritz, shoot," he bawled.

They were off again. It wasn't the way Mr. Banks had pictured it. In fact, it reminded him more of the mob scene in the *Vagabond King* than a wedding rehearsal. He gave a sigh of relief as he saw the Reverend Galsworthy enter the church, trotting like a pony and exuding geniality. Now they would get the situation in hand.

"Well, well, well," said Mr. Galsworthy. "All over, I see. That means I'm just in time. So sorry. Had a meeting. Mr. Tringle's an old hand, though." He put his arm around Mr. Tringle's shoulder and squeezed him with impersonal affection. "Do they know their stuff, Mr. Tringle? Good. Well, I'm sure it will all go off very smoothly and that it will be a beautiful wedding."

Mr. Banks could hardly believe what he heard. "But they haven't really begun to rehearse. Four of the bridal party aren't even here yet and the groom isn't here either. They tried it a couple of times and it was awful."

Mr. Galsworthy looked at his watch and clucked.

"They do all right," said Mr. Tringle. "O.K. tomorrow."

"Good," said Mr. Galsworthy. "Good. I have a meeting now. As for the groom—well, the groom is not very important at weddings, is he, my dear?" He smiled benignly at the wispy bridesmaid under the impression that she was the bride-to-be.

"You're not nervous, are you, dear?" he continued, taking the wispy girl's hand in his. "No, of course not. Have your young man call me in the morning. I'll put him through his paces. I hate to rush, but I must. Don't worry. Everything will be fine."

Mr. Banks opened his mouth. "But—" A secretarial-looking person bustled down the aisle. "Mrs. Banks? There's a phone call for you in the Rector's office. I believe it's the groom's father and mother. They're at your house and they want to know if the rehearsal's over. I think the groom is with them."

"Sure," said Mr. Tringle cheerily. "Rehearsal's all over. Tell 'em to take it easy. Everybody'll be right home."

"Don't forget to have the groom call me in the morning," said Mr. Galsworthy. "Now don't worry. It will go beautifully tomorrow. I know. You see I've done this before."

"But—" began Mr. Banks. Then he looked around. The bridal party had disappeared, bearing Kay and the wispy girl with them. Mr. and Mrs. Banks shook hands cordially with Mr. Galsworthy and followed them.

On the way out Mr. Banks noted that most of Miss Bellamy's beautifully typed seating lists had been laid on the seats of pews and abandoned. He gathered them up. With the extras there might be enough for a redistribution.

"I do hope—" said Mrs. Banks.

"So do I," agreed her husband.

They went home to dress for the party at the Club.

The last guest had gone. The last damp hand had been wrung. The bridal party had disappeared noisily to seek bigger and newer adventure. The Dunstans had left. The relatives had returned to the oblivion from which they had emerged. Mr. and Mrs. Banks were alone with the wreckage.

They sat limply in two armchairs which Mr. Banks had dragged down from upstairs. The rug was covered with confetti. The few casual tables which Mr. Massoula had left in the living room were garnished with gray rings. Here and there on the white paint of the sills were the dark signatures of cigarettes. The floral background of the reception line obliterated the fireplace. They stared at it in silence.

"She did look lovely in that going-away suit," said Mrs. Banks dreamily. "Didn't you think it was good-looking?"

Mr. Banks couldn't remember it very well. He knew she had had on something tan. There his detail stopped. But her face was etched forever on his memory as she stood on the landing waiting to throw the bride's bouquet.

"She's a darling," he said.

"Queer the Griswolds didn't come," mused Mrs. Banks. "They accepted and Jane told me they were coming."

"I don't see how you know whether they came or not."

"I know everybody that was here and everybody that wasn't," said Mrs. Banks complacently.

Mr. Banks did not question it. This woman who couldn't remember the details of the most elementary problem for five minutes would remember now and forever everyone who came, everyone who didn't—and also those who crashed the gate.

"My God," exclaimed Mrs. Banks, pressing her hand over her face. "We forgot to ask the Storers."

"We couldn't have," said Mr. Banks.

"We did, though."

"That's terrible. Couldn't we pretend we sent an invitation? You could call Esther tomorrow and ask her why she didn't come."

"I might at that," said Mrs. Banks.

There was a brief silence. "What are we going to do with all those presents?" asked Mr. Banks.

"I don't know. Somebody's got to pack them, I suppose. I think I'll just leave them as they are for a while."

"I guess that's the best thing," said Mr. Banks.

They lapsed into exhausted silence. In the brain of each a projector was unreeling the film of the day's events. It would have amazed them if they could have known how different the films were.

In another compartment of Mr. Banks' brain an adding machine was relentlessly at work. The figures came pouring out and each time they were greater than before.

"Didn't the decorations in the church look too lovely?" asked Mrs. Banks.

Mr. Banks was startled to discover that he had not even noticed if there were any decorations in the church. It was a relief to know that someone had checked on that dog-robber Tim.

"They were beautiful," he said simply.

"Mr. Tim did a wonderful job considering how little money we gave him to work with," said Mrs. Banks. Her husband started, then pressed his lips together and made no comment.

"I suppose," said Mrs. Banks, "we ought to get out the vacuum cleaner and not leave this whole mess for Delilah tomorrow. I'll go up and change my dress."

Mr. Banks followed her upstairs glumly. Like a fog blowing in from the sea, he could feel the first wisps of depression fingering into his soul.

Here was the place where she had stood. He paused and looked over the rail at the confetti-strewn hall. Queer about places and houses. They remained the same yet they were never the same. By no stretch of the imagination was this the spot from which Kay had tossed her flowers to the waving arms below.

He continued up the stairs, thinking of all the money and energy that was wasted each year visiting the scenes of great events under the impression that they were still the same places.

At the door of the spare room where the presents were on display, he paused, then lit the light and went in. This morning it had been a gay, exciting place, full of anticipation and promise of things to come. The animating spirit was gone. Now it was just a bare room with card tables along the walls covered with china and glassware. It was as impersonal as a store.

He tried to shake off the cloud that was settling over him. In the bathroom a single bottle of champagne rested quietly in the washbasin. It had been put there by someone just before Mr.

Massoula ran out. Heaven knew what for. It was still cold. For a moment he debated whether to open it. Then he turned, went downstairs and got out the vacuum cleaner.

An hour later the last particle of confetti had been transferred to the bulging bag of the machine. They sat once more in their chairs in the living room gazing with exhausted faces at the banked greens in front of the fireplace.

On the floor near the edge of the rug Mr. Banks spied a few bits of confetti that the cleaner had overlooked. He rose to pick them up. There seemed to be more just under the edge. He turned back the corner and disclosed a solid mat of multicolored paper.

Without comment he dropped the rug back into place. Mrs. Banks was watching, but said nothing. He went quietly up to the bathroom and drew the cork in the last remaining bottle. From the spare room he selected two of Kay's new champagne glasses and returned to his wife.

Carefully he filled the two glasses and handed one to Mrs. Banks. Behind the floral background the clock on the mantle struck twelve. The whistle of a train from the city hooted in the distance as it rounded the curve into the Fairview Manor station. A dog was barking somewhere.

"How," said Mr. Banks raising his glass.

"How," said Mrs. Banks.

*   *

Your leaving us has left a great blank in our lives. . . .

KING GEORGE VI

from

A LETTER TO PRINCESS ELIZABETH*

. . . I WAS SO PROUD of you & thrilled at having you so close to me on our long walk in Westminster Abbey, but when I handed your hand to the Archbishop I felt that I had lost something very precious. You

---

* This letter was written in November, 1947, soon after Princess Elizabeth, now Queen Elizabeth II, married Prince Philip.

were so calm & composed during the Service & said your words with
such conviction, that I knew everything was all right.

I am so glad you wrote & told Mummy that you think the long
wait before your engagement & the long time before the wedding was
for the best. I was rather afraid that you had thought I was being
hard hearted about it. I was so anxious for you to come to South
Africa as you knew. Our family, us four, the "Royal Family" must
remain together with additions of course at suitable moments!! I
have watched you grow up all these years with pride under the skill-
ful direction of Mummy, who as you know is the most marvellous
person in the World in my eyes, & I can, I know, always count on you,
& now Philip, to help us in our work. Your leaving us has left a
great blank in our lives but do remember that your old home is still
yours & do come back to it as much & as often as possible. I can see
that you are sublimely happy with Philip which is right but don't
forget us is the wish of

Your ever loving & devoted

Papa

*   *

Have you forgotten who I am?

SHOLEM ASCH

FATHERS-IN-LAW

OLD GLICKSTEIN, whom the East Side knew familiarly as "the
grandfather," had not always had the same bitter and contemp-
tuous attitude toward American radicalism and its future. Many
years before, when he had been accounted one of the most brilliant
orators and most active spirits in "the movement," his estimate
of its worth had been very different. But this had declined with his
own reputation, which was now based entirely on his past. And he
affected to regret his own record, for when anyone reminded him
of the days of his glory, he made a deprecatory gesture and said,
angrily: "That's enough, now!" He was, of course, glad of the
opportunity to make the gesture, and to exclaim "That's enough,
now!"

Glickstein's own children were to blame for his embitterment and despair. In public he poured out the vials of his wrath and his immeasurable contempt on "the big shots," the parvenus who had taken over the movement, had betrayed and degraded it, so that there was nothing left for a pure spirit like himself but "to leave the field of battle." In private he was quite clear as to the real causes of his disastrous decline, namely, his children.

For actually, while he spoke derisively of "these newfangled parlor pinks," who were as ignorant as they were pusillanimous, and as hypocritical as they were egostistic, he would not quite relinquish some degree of credit for having been their teacher. If someone mentioned in his presence the name of one of the new "leaders," "the grandfather" would crow: "That man? Why, I was the one who taught him the theories of Bakunin and Kropotkin. Whatever he knows he owes to me!" He had, indeed, been the teacher of an entire generation; it was not his fault if his pupils had declined from his lofty standards.

Of his own children, however, he could not even say that he had been their teacher. To begin with, he had never had the time for it. His days had been spent in cafés and at meetings, at conventions and conferences. Apart from the matter of time, he had never been interested in his own children. He had left their upbringing to their mother; that was her business. And she, though she was the wife of the well-known public worker and had never (so it was whispered) submitted to the indignity of a formal marriage ceremony, but had become his common-law wife in vindication of the purity of their love, turned out to be an exceedingly ordinary mother; she loved her children as every ordinary mother does and let them have their own way, even when they showed an alarming interest in religion.

It must be admitted, too, that the children of the great Glickstein were not particularly interesting. First there came an uninterrupted row of daughters, who shot up with unaccountable rapidity, like strange watery growths. Glickstein always referred to them as "onions," for a mysterious reason which he never explained. In their childhood their attitude toward him was one of fear rather than respect. Glickstein had a voice which had originally been deep and resonant, but which excessive oratory had cracked and hoarsened, so that it gave forth the terrifying tremolo of an overused trumpet. He had enormous black eye-

brows which completely overshadowed his eyes. His face was
clean shaven, so that his nose stood forth from it without any
distracting substructure. His build, too, was impressive; so that
for children the first reaction was one of fear. On the rare oc-
casions when he would be home, he would stride about with
his hands thrust deep into his trouser pockets; and he had
one phrase for the family: "I want quiet!" When they heard
that phrase, uttered in the deep, cracked tremolo issuing from
under the commanding beak, there was quiet. The laughter of
the children, the chattering of the mother, came to an abrupt
end. And if it happened that the phrase failed, once in a way, it
was followed by a single, tremendous word: "Sarah!" That settled
it. "Sarah!" was the ultimatum.

All this lasted through the years when the children were at
school. Then a change began. The first girl graduated, found a
job as a stenographer, and contributed seven dollars of her salary
toward the upkeep of the house; the remainder she kept for clothes
and pocket money. The second girl went to work in a millinery
shop and also contributed something toward the upkeep of the
house. Before long Glickstein began to feel that he was not lord
and master in his own house; there were others sharing the responsibility and demanding a share in the authority. Without putting it into words, they presented him with an alternative; they
could move to another home, where the imperious "I want quiet"
would not fall on their ears. The unspoken argument sank home.

The girls had never understood what their father's occupation
was and what he made a living from. Their mother had tried to
explain to them that their father was "a great man," "a public
figure," "a leader." The words left no particular impression. If
their father was "a great man," then "a great man" was a form of
occupation, a trade like any other. They would have preferred a
more familiar and more impressive occupation; they would have
liked to be able to tell their friends that their father was a manu-
facturer, or a storekeeper. One of them, the milliner, feeling uncomfortable at having to describe her father's business as that of
"a great man," represented him to her boy friend as a landlord.
She thought this more impressive, and more likely to win her boy
friend's respect; nor was she mistaken.

The boys who followed in the Glickstein family, after the row of girls, were more interesting. The youngest of them was particularly promising. By the time he reached high school age his father mapped out for him the career of poet. The boy was quiet, thoughtful, and shy; he took after his mother in appearance and spirit. But Glickstein sustained the greatest shock of his life when, one evening, his son reproached him with never attending temple services and never making the Friday evening benediction at table, like the fathers of his boy friends.

"You aren't a good Jew," said the boy firmly. "A Jew attends temple and makes the benediction every Friday evening."

"Who told you that? Who told you that?" asked the father in his cracked baritone. And as always when something disturbing happened in the house he let out a trumpet call:

"Sarah! Sarah!"

Sarah happened to be busy in the kitchen at the moment. When the trumpet peal came to her ears she knew that a crisis was at hand, and she came running in with perspiring face and rolled-up sleeves.

"What's the matter?" she asked, terrified.

"Go on now, tell your mother what you told me," stormed Glickstein. "Tell her. Repeat every word."

Faltering, the boy said:

"I told pop he isn't a Jew. A Jew goes to temple and makes the benediction every Friday night."

"Do you hear that, Sarah? Do you hear it?" thundered Glickstein.

"What's so terrible about it?" asked Mrs. Glickstein. "You know what boys are? They hear something in a friend's house, and they repeat it."

"What's so terrible about that!" mimicked Glickstein in despair. "What's so terrible about that! I'm not a Jew because I don't go to temple and I don't make the benediction on Friday night. That's nothing to you!"

"Well, what harm would it do you if you went to temple once in a while, for the boy's sake, or if you stayed home Friday evenings, so that the children could stay home instead of being always with strangers?" Ancient longings spoke out of Mrs. Glickstein, also the cumulative effect of receiving most of her household money from her daughters instead of from her husband.

"What's that you said?" asked Mr. Glickstein. "Did you say temple to me? Did you suggest that I attend temple services? Have you forgotten who I am?" And Mr. Glickstein took off the glasses which he had had to use of late, and worked his tremendous eyebrows up and down. The habit of years asserted itself in Mrs. Glickstein, and she shrank from her husband.

"I didn't say anything," she stammered. "I only said, for the boy's sake—I mean—I didn't say anything. You never went to temple, and there's no reason why you should go now."

"And to think," said Mr. Glickstein, "that my life has been spent with this woman!"

Mr. Glickstein had not noticed how his wife, year after year, had yielded to her children and had permitted, or even encouraged, the infiltration of the Jewish religious atmosphere into his home. It had begun with the cooking. Whenever a Jewish festival came round, there would be on the table the appropriate dishes —dumplings, *matzoth*, or *pirogens*. Whatever Mr. Glickstein's views on Jewish ritual, he had never entertained any distaste for the appropriate dishes. On the contrary, he had always enjoyed them; and his enjoyment of them helped him to forget their religious associations. But coming home one Friday evening, he was startled to observe on the table not only the stuffed fish and white bread appropriate to the Sabbath, but also the lit candles which bespoke the woman's benediction, and the glass of wine for the benediction by the master of the house.

"Sarah!" he declaimed. "What is this?"

"What do you care? The boy likes a Jewish touch about the house. What harm is there in that?"

"What *harm* is there in that? What harm is there in *that*?"

But at this point the girls interfered.

"What business is it of yours?" said the older one, who contributed seven dollars a week to the upkeep of the home. "Sam wants the Friday night benediction. I'm paying for the wine. Go ahead, Sam."

Glickstein collapsed in a corner, at a loss for words. Sam, pallid and terrified, put on his hat, turned the pages of the prayer book, and began to stammer the Hebrew words like a little boy in the first class at a Hebrew school:

"And—and—it was—it was—morning—it was morning—and evening—"

"Ignoramus! Heathen!" thundered Mr. Glickstein. "You don't even know how to say the Friday evening benediction!"

"Did you ever teach him how?" wailed his wife.

Glickstein strode over to the table, grabbed the wine-cup from Sam's hand, shoved the boy to one side, and said the benediction from beginning to end without once looking at the text in the prayer book.

He not only *said* the benediction. He chanted it with all the roulades and the grace notes of the tradition. His wife stared at him with shining and grateful eyes, and his children were dumb-struck with astonishment and admiration.

Coming home late one evening, Mr. Glickstein found as-sembled in the parlor a group of young people. He paid no par-ticular attention to them, but passed through the room and went upstairs. He was accustomed by now to feeling himself more or less of a stranger in his own home. But before he had begun to undress, his wife burst in and imparted to him the news that Masha, the milliner, was engaged to Mr. Borenstein, a wholesale dealer in groceries and a fine, decent young man. Mr. Glickstein listened in a stupor. In itself, the engagement of his daughter seemed to him to be a matter of minor importance. He experi-enced a faint satisfaction in the thought of his daughter's happi-ness; he was also aware of a more distinct inward disturbance at the thought of the loss to the household income. But he relied on his wife to straighten matters out. The management of the house had always been her department. She had never failed to adapt herself to changing conditions; she would not fail now. And there his interest ended. However, as a matter of ordinary courtesy, he went down to the parlor and suffered himself to be introduced to the young man. Prospective son-in-law and pros-pective father-in-law shook hands, said "How do you do?" looked at each other awkwardly, and sat down. Glickstein could think of nothing to say regarding the wholesale grocery line, and the young man had never heard of Kropotkin and Bakunin. The first five minutes determined the character of future relations between

them: a remote and wordless friendliness. It was always a cordial
"How do you do?" a handshake, an interval of embarrassed silence,
and withdrawal by mutual consent and with mutual relief. Glickstein avoided his home more than ever before. The place had
become intolerably noisy. It seemed to him that his daughter's
young man was literally taking the house by storm. Innumerable
young people turned up nearly every evening; all of them had
loud voices; all of them laughed immoderately at nothing. It
was a madhouse, and to avoid a nervous breakdown, or a quarrel
with the young people, or both, Glickstein gave his home a wide
berth.

He did not occupy himself with the preparations for the wedding, but left that to his wife and the young couple. Let them
do what they wanted. For his part, he waited gloomily for the
whole wretched, confused, noisy business to be over, so that his
life might resume its normal tenor.

The bride and bridegroom hired a hall, musicians, a wedding
jester, and a "reverend." The bridegroom's family, with its many
ramifications, was of Galician origin, Jews attached to the traditional ritual. They insisted on a wedding in the good old style.
And since Glickstein had washed his hands of the business, and
his wife was only too delighted to have a real, hearty Jewish wedding, there was no disagreement anywhere.

Had it not been for his wife's insistence, Glickstein would not
even have come to the wedding. Reluctantly he donned the Prince
Albert which he once used to wear on the lecture platform, and
just as reluctantly he entered the cab which took them to the
wedding hall. The place swarmed with excited and noisy guests,
practically all of them relatives and friends of the bridegroom.
The young men wore tuxedos, the young women extravagantly
décolleté evening dress. All afternoon and evening they danced.
Glickstein wandered about like a lost soul; he knew no one, and
no one knew him. Sarah was happy in the company of the other
mother-in-law, a pious old Jewess who wore the traditional wig;
from time to time Glickstein caught sight of them in earnest conversation and wondered what it was they could talk about hour
after hour without a letup. As for himself, he moved about in a
vast loneliness, punctuated by occasional, convulsive "How-do-

you-do's?" Finally he sat down in a corner, and resigned himself to a long vigil.

The moment of the ceremony arrived at last. The canopy was erected in the middle of the hall; the two fathers-in-law were finally introduced to each other. Glickstein saw before him an old, trembling Jew, with a gray beard and gray earlocks. Apparently he, like Glickstein, had been hiding in a corner, feeling equally alien to this crowd of young people. Timidly the old Jew put out his hand, and said:

"*Sholom aleichem,* greetings."

Glickstein was petrified. For an instant he felt like rushing out of the hall. Who was this incredible fossil? But a feeling of compassion succeeded his first reaction of amazement. He put out his hand, too, and answered:

"*Aleichem sholom,* greetings!"

When the ceremony under the bridal canopy was completed, the fathers-in-law were forgotten again. A young man whom Glickstein did not know courteously found a place for him at the dinner table; the other father-in-law seemed to have disappeared. To right and left of Glickstein there were riotous conversation, laughter, much eating and drinking; but he might as well have been a thousand miles away for all the attention he received. When dinner was over and the tables were cleared away for the resumption of the dancing, Glickstein looked for a quiet corner whence he could slip out of the hall unobserved. And as he wandered between the stacked chairs he felt someone plucking timidly at his elbow. He turned and beheld the trembling old Jew with the gray beard and earlocks, the bridegroom's father.

"The bridegroom's father-in-law seems to be all alone," murmured the bridegroom's father.

"Certainly not!" answered Glickstein, irritably.

"I mean," stammered the other, in an imploring tone of voice, "I mean the young people have forgotten the old."

"Yes! Yes! We're forgotten," said Glickstein, dramatically.

"Let's sit down somewhere and take a drink," suggested the bridegroom's father, humbly. "We're the two fathers-in-law, aren't we, the old-timers? We belong together."

All the free-thinker, the radical, the anti-religious orator rose in

Glickstein. What had he to do with this old pietist loon, this superannuated representative of superstition and reaction? Was not this the world he had been fighting all his life as a soldier of progress, liberty, and enlightenment? But from beneath these impulses of his career rose others, deeper and stronger, also released by the sight of the gray beard, the earlocks, the skull cap. Glickstein remembered something—he did not know exactly what. He took the old man's arm.

"Yes, yes," he answered, "we belong together. We don't belong to those—those—" he indicated the young people in tuxedos and décolleté—"those dancers, those ignoramuses and vulgarians. What do they know? What have they ever achieved? But you and I, yes, you and I, the old fathers-in-law, we understand each other."

Glass in hand they sat down in a corner, and with knees touching they drank to each other's health.

AN AGING MAN

How pleasant it is for a father to sit at his child's board. It is like an aged man reclining under the shadow of an oak he has planted.

SIR WALTER SCOTT

V. S. PRITCHETT

JUST A LITTLE MORE

THEY WERE SPEAKING in low voices in the kitchen.

"How is he? Has he said what he is going to do?" she asked her husband. "Is there any news?"

"None at all," the husband whispered. "He's coming down now. He says he just wants a house by the sea, in a place where the air is bracing and the water's soft and there's a good variety of fish."

"Sh-h-h! Why do we whisper like this? Here he comes. Get the plates."

A moment later, the very old gentleman, her father-in-law, was standing in the doorway, staring and smiling. He was short and very fat, and one of the things he liked to do was to pause in the doorway of a room and look it over from ceiling to floor. In the old days, his family or his workers at the factory used to stiffen nervously when he did this, wondering where his eye would stop.

"Excuse me being rude," he said at last. "What a lovely smell."

"Take your father in," the wife said. "These plates are hot. Go into the dining room, Grandpa."

"I'm just looking at your refrigerator, darling," the old gentleman said. "Very nice. It's a Pidex, I see. Is that a good make? I mean is it good—does it work well? . . . I'm glad to hear that. Did you get it from the Pidex people? . . . Ah, I thought you did. Good people."

The son, who was in his fifties, took the old gentleman by the elbow and moved him slowly into the dining room. The old gentleman blew his nose.

"No. Your mother's hands were as cold as ice when I got to

223

her," said the old gentleman, astonished by a memory. "But she had gone. Where do I go? Do I sit here?"

He sat down very suddenly at the table. Although he weighed close to two hundred pounds, his clothes hung loosely on him, for he had once weighed much more. His nostrils had spread and reddened over a skin that was greenish and violet on the cheeks but as pale and stringy as a chicken's at the neck.

His daughter-in-law and two grandchildren brought in the joint and the vegetables. The grandchildren were called Richard and Helen. They were in their teens. Their mouths watered when they saw the food on the table, and they leaned toward it, but kept their eyes politely on the old man, like elderly listeners.

"I hope you haven't cooked anything special for me," the old man said. "I was just saying I talk too much when I come for a weekend here, and I eat too much. It's living alone—having no one to talk to, and so forth, and you can't be bothered to eat—that's the point. What a lovely piece of beef that is! Wonderful. I haven't seen a joint of beef like that for centuries. A small bit of loin of lamb we might have, but my wife can't digest it." He often forgot that his wife was dead. "And it doesn't keep. I put it in the larder and I forget and it goes wrong." His big face suddenly crinkled like an apple, with disgust.

"Well, well, I don't know, I'm sure," he went on, gazing at the beef his son was now carving. "I suppose it's all right. What do you call a joint like that?" He pointed across the table to his grandson. "We used to have beef when your father was a boy, Richard. Your father was a boy once. You can't imagine that, can you? Aitchbone, was it? I can't remember. I don't know where your mother used to get it. Bell's, I suppose. I don't know what we paid for it. Sixpence a pound, perhaps. We can't do it now; it's the price."

His son passed him a plate. The old man hesitated, not knowing whether to pass it on and not wanting to. "If this is for me, don't give me any more," he said. "I hardly eat anything nowadays. If I could have just a little fat . . ." Relieved, he kept the plate.

"Pass the vegetables to Grandpa," said his daughter-in-law to Helen.

"Grandpa, vegetables?" Helen said, looking younger now as she spoke.

"Oh," said the old gentleman. He had gone into a dream. "I was just watching you carving," he said to his son. "I was looking at your face. You've got just the expression of your Great-Grand-father Harry. I remember him when I was a little boy. Father took me to see him—it was one morning. He took me down to a warehouse, would it be?—in the docks or harbor—a factory, per-haps—and he lifted me up to a window and I saw him, just his face, it was only a minute. He was slitting up herrings; it was a curing place."

"Fish! I knew it." His daughter-in-law laughed.

"The sea is in our blood," said her husband. Everyone was laughing.

"What is this? What are you laughing at? What have I said?" the old gentleman asked, smiling. "Are you getting at me?"

"That is where you get your taste for kippers," said the daugh-ter-in-law to her husband.

"Ah, kippers!" said the old gentleman, delighted by his strange success. "How are you for fish in this neighborhood? Do you get good fish? I sometimes feel like a piece of fish. But there doesn't seem to be the fish about, these days. I don't know why that is. No, I went up to the fishmonger on Tuesday and I looked. He came up to me, and I said, 'Good morning.' 'Good morning, Mr. Hopkins,' he said. 'What can I do for you?' 'Do for me?' I said. 'Give me a fortnight in Monte Carlo.' He exploded. I said, 'What's happened to you? What's wrong?' 'What do you mean, Mr. Hop-kins?' he said. 'I mean, where's your fish?' I said. 'That's not what I call fish. Not f-i-s-h.' He knew what I meant. 'Sole,' he said. 'Dover sole,' I said. 'Mr. Hopkins,' he said, 'I haven't had a Dover sole for a fortnight. Not one I'd sell *you*. Lemon sole,' he said, and something—grayling, did he say? Well, that's the way it is. And so we go on."

"No," the old man said after a moment. "Kitty, your mother, my wife, was very fond of fish. When we were first married, and so forth, we came down from the north— How old are you, my boy? Fifty-seven? You're not fifty-seven!—it was just before you were born, and my wife said, 'I'd give anything for an oyster.' The train didn't get in till eight, but we were young and reckless in those days. I didn't care a damn for anyone. I was ready to knock the world over. I was in a good crib, five pounds a week at Week-ley's—before Hollins took them over. All expenses. I thought I was Julius Caesar—marvellous, isn't it? Do I mean him? And we went across the road and your mother said, 'Come on—' "

The son interrupted, picking up the story. "And a busdriver leaned out of his cab and said, 'Watch out, lady. Babies are scarce this year.' Mother told me."

"I'm sure she didn't," said the old gentleman, blushing a little. "Your father's imagination, Richard!"

"Yes, but what happened?" asked his daughter-in-law.

"And there was a little place, a real old London fish place—sawdust on the floor, I suppose they had in those days. Crossfield . . . Cross . . . Crofty—I forget the name—and we had a dozen oysters each, maybe I had a couple of dozen; I don't remember now, I couldn't say. Frederick's—*that* was the name of the place. Frederick's. And I suppose we must have followed it with Dover sole. They used to do a wonderful Welsh rabbit."

"And that is how I was born," said the son. "Let me give you some more beef, Father."

"Me? Oh, no. I don't eat what I used to. It's living alone, and these new teeth of mine—I've had a lot of trouble with them. Don't give me any more. I don't mind a couple of slices—well, just another. And some fat. I like a piece of fat. That's what I feel. You go home and you get to the house, and it's dark. And it's empty. You go in and the boiler's low—I don't seem to get the right coke. Do you get good coke here? You look at it all and you look in the larder and you can't be bothered. There's a chop, a bit of bread and cheese, perhaps. And you think, Well, if this is all there is in life, you may as well finish it. I'm in a rut down in that place. I've got to get away. I can't breathe there. I'd like to get down to the sea."

"I think you ought to go where you have friends," said his daughter-in-law.

The old gentleman put his knife and fork down. "Friends?" he said, in a stern voice, raising his chin. "I have no friends. All my friends are dead." He said this with indignation and contempt.

"But what about your friend Rogers, in Devonshire?" said his son.

"Rogers? I was disappointed in Rogers. He's aged. He's let himself go. I hadn't seen him for twenty-five years. When I saw him, I said to him, 'Why, what's the matter with you? Trying to pretend you are an old man?" He looked at me. He'd let his mustache go long and gray. I wouldn't have known him. And there was something else. A funny thing. It upset me." The old gentleman's jolly face shrivelled up again, with horror. "The hairs in his nose had gone gray!" he said. "I couldn't bear it. He was very kind, *and* his wife was. We had lunch. Soup of some kind—tomato, or maybe oxtail—and then a piece of lamb, potatoes, and cauliflower. Oh, very nice. I've forgotten what the dessert was—some cream, I suppose, they have good cream there—and coffee, of course. Cheese . . . I don't remember. Afterward—and this is what upsets me about old people—they wanted a rest. Every day, after lunch, they go off and have a sleep—every day. Can you imagine that? I couldn't stand that. Terrible."

"It's good to have a siesta," said the son.

"I couldn't. I never have. I just can't," said the old gentleman, in a panic. "The other afternoon after lunch, I forget what I had, a chop, I think—I couldn't be bothered to cook vegetables, well, on your own you don't, that's the point—I dropped off. I don't know how long, and when I woke up it was dark. I couldn't see anything. I didn't know where I was. 'Where am I?' I said. 'What day is it?' And I reached out for my wife. I thought I was in bed, and I called out 'Kitty, Kitty, where are you?' and then I said, 'Oh.' It came back to me. I'm here. In this room. I couldn't move. I got up and put on the light. I was done up. I poured myself out a small glass of port. I felt I had to. It was shocking. And shocking dreams."

He stared and then suddenly he turned to his daughter-in-law and said, in another voice, "Those sandwiches I shan't forget. Egg, wasn't it? You remember." He wagged a finger at Helen. "Helen, your mother is a wonder at egg sandwiches. It was the first time in my life I'd ever eaten them. The day we put Kitty away, you remember, she came down and made egg sandwiches. What is the secret of it? She won't tell. Butter, I suppose? Richard, what is the word I want? You know—'smashing,' I suppose you'd call them."

He paused, and his eyes grew vaguer. "No," he went on, "I don't know what I'll do. I think I shall go to the sea and look around. I shall get a list of houses, and put my furniture in store. I could live with your brother John, or you. I know I could, but it would be wrong. You have your own lives. I want my independence. Life is beginning for me—that is what I feel. I feel I would like to go on a cruise round the world. There was a house at Bexhill I saw. They wanted seven thousand for it. I felt it would suit me."

"Seven thousand!" said his son, in alarm. "Where would you get seven thousand from?"

"Oh," said the old gentleman sharply, "I should raise it."

"Raise it!" exclaimed the son. "How?"

"That's just it," said the old gentleman cheerfully. "I don't know. The way will open up. You, perhaps, or John."

Husband and wife looked down the table at each other in consternation.

"Shall we go upstairs and have some coffee?" she said.

"That son of yours, that Richard—did you see what he ate?" said the old gentleman as he got up from the table. "Marvellous, isn't it? Of course, things are better than when I was a boy. I feel everything is better. We used to go to school with twopence for a pie. Not every day—twice a week. The other days, we just looked at the shopwindow. Pies piled up. And once a week— Friday, I expect—it was herrings in the evening. The fisherwomen came calling them in the street, eighteen a shilling, fresh out of the sea. Salmon I used to be fond of. D'you ever have salmon?"

He paused in the doorway and looked at the carpet on the stairs and at the wallpaper. "I like rich things," he said, nodding to the carpet. "That gravy was good. Luscious grapes, pears, all large fruits I like. Those Christmas displays at the meat market —turkeys and geese by the thousand there used to be. I always used to bring your mother something. A few chops, two or three pairs of kippers. And so forth. I don't know what."

"Upstairs to the sitting room, Father," said the son. "I'm coming in a minute with the coffee."

The son went into the kitchen, and the whispering began again.

"Seven thousand!" he said. "Seven million wouldn't keep him!"

"Sh-h-h," said his wife. "It's a daydream."

"But what are we going to do?"

In a few minutes, he took the coffee upstairs. The old gentleman was sitting down, with his waistcoat undone and his thumbs twiddling on his stomach.

"I've been thinking about you," the old gentleman said rebukingly. "You've lost weight. You don't eat. You worry too much. My wife used to worry."

The son passed a coffee cup to him.

"Is there a lot of sugar in it? Thank you," the old man said. He gave it a stir, took a sip, and then held the cup out. "I think I'll have a couple of spoonfuls more."

*　　　*

He's takin' me off to a home, Effie. I won't go.

ROBERT COATES
Let's Not Talk About It Now

THE OLD MAN was sitting by the window in the big leather rocker when Eve came into the parlor. He didn't seem to hear her or see her, and she had a moment of sharp realization of how really old he looked, with the thin hands lying listless in his lap and the pale, shrunk-skinned, vacant face turned half away from her towards the window. And the parlor was the coldest room in the place, and the colder because they usually kept it shut in the winter; she couldn't help wondering why he had picked it to sit in, when he had his own cozy quarters on the south side of the farmhouse. But then that was the way he had gotten lately: there were times when it was almost like what Roy said, and you'd think he was actually hiding from people, from the habit he'd taken of creeping off into odd corners and places you'd never expect to find him. Roy was her husband, and he was inclined to be a little impatient with the old man.

She was a short, plump woman, round-faced and very neat-looking, with prim blue eyes behind rimless spectacles. "Hello, father," she said. She made her voice bright and cheerful, as she always did when she talked to him. "I've been looking all over for you. What you doing, just sitting?" At the sound he turned his head quickly, and she knew she must have startled him, for his eyes stared at her blankly for what seemed a full second or two before he answered her.

"Why—it's Effie!" he said, as if she were the last person in the world he'd expected to see. He had got into a way of talking from the back of his mouth, so that the words came out heavy and mumbling. "I was just sittin' here," he went on. "I was thinkin'. I was thinkin' about them days back in Fayette. You was too young to remember much, I guess, but there was a big tree there, a big beech it was, down to the south side of the house, and your mother was always at me to cut it down. Said it was too near the house. Made the rooms damp, she said. But I never would. I was always a great one for trees." He stopped and turned to look out the window again. All you could see from there was the flat expanse of the north meadow, its grass barren-brown and crisp after the repeated frosts, and beyond that the rise of ground towards the hills at the end of the valley. There was a little snow here and there, left from last week's snow-fall, in the sheltered places. "I was wonderin' if that tree's still standin'," he said.

Eve had been listening with an air of bright attention; she made it a rule never to interrupt the old man, no matter how rambling his talk might become. But now when he paused she cut in at once. "That *was* a long time ago, father, wasn't it?" she said. "I'm surprised you'd remember it. But we've got to get ready to go over to the Wallises now—you know I told you we were going there for Sunday dinner? And it's a good long drive, so Roy wanted to get started early." She stopped with her voice raised a little, expectantly. But the old man didn't move. "Roy's getting the car out now," she finished. "And you know how he hates to be kept waiting. Do you want me to help you get your coat on?"

He stared at her, and a stubborn look came into his face, that stubborn childish look she dreaded. "I'd ruther not go, Effie," he said, shaking his head slowly. "You folks go. You just leave me here."

It took an effort to keep her voice cheerful. "But, father!" she said. "How *can* we go if you don't? We can't leave you all alone here. And the Wallises are expecting us." It always made her a little panicky when he got one of his stubborn streaks on, and now she heard the front door open and looked out into the hall.

Roy had just come in. He was a tall man, raw-boned and a little awkward in his movements, with straight black hair, pale eyes, and a dry, freckled skin. "Lord, it's cold," he said, as soon as he noticed his wife. He had his overcoat on, but he had taken off his hat, and he was rummaging in the shelf over the clothes closet by the door. "Where's that fur cap of mine? I be damned if I don't think I'll wear it today. Keep my ears warm, anyway."

"But, Roy," Eve protested mechanically. She was still thinking of her father. "With the heater on? You don't want the Wallises to think we come in a sleigh, do you?"

"I don't care about that," Roy said. For the first time he really looked at his wife. "Where's your coat?" he demanded. "Ain't you ready yet? Where's your pa?"

Eve took a step or two towards him, down the hall. "Roy, he says he don't want to go. He's in the parlor. Roy, I wish you would speak to him."

"Me speak to him?" Roy said. He was still feeling around on the shelf, looking for his cap. "He's your pa, ain't he?" he said. "You're the one that's supposed to handle him, ain't you? Why, whenever I even so much as open my mouth to him—"

"Roy, that's different. That time you were quarreling."

"Who wouldn't, I'd like to know? And what am I supposed to do now? Listen here, I left that motor running outside, too. That's using up gas." He stood looking at her for a moment, while Eve studied him anxiously, then he started past her towards the parlor. "All right," he said. "I'll talk to him."

"Don't be hard on him, Roy," Eve said. Roy paid no attention. He walked into the parlor and headed straight across it for the old man's chair. "Now, father, we've really *got* to go," Eve began as she came into the room behind him, but the old man paid no attention to her either. He was watching Roy, his head cocked sidewise in an odd awkward fashion and his thin neck stretched stiff and wary as a bird's.

"I ain't goin', Roy. You can't make me," he said. His hands were clutched tight on the arms of the chair. Roy kept walking.

"Come on, Pop. No foolin' now," Roy said. Eve had stopped at the door, and all she could see of Roy was his back, big and burly-looking in the heavy overcoat. His voice, though it wasn't gentle, wasn't rough; he walked towards her father with the

steady, unhurried, undisturbing stride of a man who is approaching a fractious animal and doesn't want to alarm it.

"Roy!" Eve called, for no reason that she could think of, and
she saw the old man's eyes flick to hers for an instant, then they
went back to Roy's face again. As Roy neared him his lips began
to move but he wasn't saying anything, or not anything Eve
could hear; it wasn't till Roy reached his side that his voice came.
"Well, now," Roy said as he might have said to a horse he was
trying to quiet, and with a movement as quick as it was certain
he bent down, ran his hands under the old man's arms at the
armpits, and started to lift him out of the chair. At his touch,
something almost like frenzy seemed to take hold of the old man.

"Effie! Effie!" he cried in a kind of feeble shout. "He can't
take me. Don't let him take me. I won't go. You can't take me
to no home, I belong here and Effie won't—Effie, don't let him.
Don't let him take me." He had flung himself back in the chair,
wrenching out of Roy's grasp, and now he pitched forward again,
craning out past Roy's body and peering at her. "Effie!" he called
again. "Effie!"

It was all so sudden, so unexpected, that for a moment Eve
could not move. "I ain't taking you no such place, you old fool,"
Roy was saying. "Not this time." He was laughing as he spoke,
but it was mainly with exasperation, and Eve could see the red
that must have been in his face come creeping around till his
neck was dark with it. Then he bent down to seize the old man
again; until then Eve had stood stock-still, but when she saw
Roy's hands fall on the old man's shoulders something carried
her forward. She found herself between the two men, staring up at
Roy's face and then down at her father's. "Roy! Father!" she
said. "What is it?" Then she felt the old man's hand thrust into
hers. "He's takin' me off to a home, Effie. I won't go," he said.

"Hush, father," she started to say, but she wasn't looking at
him. She was looking at Roy. "That's just nonsense—"

" 'Tain't nonsense!" the old man cut in, his voice rising. "He's
said so. He told me—"

"—We're just going to the Wallises'," Eve had gone on, but
the old man was still talking, and above his voice she could hear
Roy's raised too. "That's a lie!" Roy was shouting. "It's a damned
lie!"

" 'Tain't so," the old man shouted back, and it wasn't till then, in the midst of the clatter of voices, that Eve really grasped what they were talking about. She could feel the blood flare into her face and then drain out again. "Did you, Roy?" she demanded. "Did you say that to him?"

There was a pause before Roy spoke. He was looking down at the old man and he didn't raise his eyes. "Well, you heard him," he said.

"But, Roy, did you?"

"I tell you, you heard him. Who's to say what I did, him or me?"

"But I'm asking you, Roy."

Roy's face was still turned away, and it was so long before he looked up that she thought he wasn't going to answer at all. When he did, his eyes went all around the room before they met hers. "Well, by Jesus, I did then!" he burst out. There was rage in his face but there was embarrassment too, and seeing him, Eve knew what was troubling him—them here and the old man between them, and they quarreling about him. It was troubling her too. "Roy!" she cried. "Let's not talk about it." But there was no stopping him now.

"You brought it up, and by God, you'll have it!" he said. "I've taken enough. Him and you, and him sitting there. All I hear is about him, what he'll eat and what he won't eat. What he wants and what he don't want. And me working. By God, sometimes I wonder—" "Roy, please!" she said, but he didn't seem to hear her. "—And now when all I ask is to get his coat on. To go out with us," he went on. "I tell you there's a place for him. There's a place he belongs and it ain't here!"

"Roy, please!" Eve cried at him again, and she could feel her father's fingers twisting in hers. "I told you," the old man was saying. "Hear him, Effie? Hear him tell it?" But all she could see was Roy's shouting face and his eyes that were so hard with hate that it was like running head-on into a stone wall. A hate, she realized now, that was directed at her instead of at her father, and at the thought of that something like terror came over her. Without knowing quite what she was doing she wrenched her hand free. "Be still, father!" she cried, and even as she said it she knew it was a voice she had never used with him before.

"Please, Roy! Please!" she said, and she held both hands out before her. "Roy, please."

"Please?" he yelled, his voice jerking higher, and he lifted one hand in so savage a gesture that for a moment she thought he was going to strike her. But instead he turned sharply away, took a quick step or two and turned back again. He stood looking down at her. "Let's not talk now," Eve said.

Roy said nothing for a while; no one said anything. For a while it was so still that the whole house seemed empty of sound, and what noises Eve heard came from outside it—the faint scrape of a branch in the wind, and the rush of the wind itself, and the feeling of broad-reaching space it carried with it. It was Roy who spoke first. "Well, God's sakes, then," he said, but his voice wasn't angry any more. "Here's us talking and there's that car running outside all this time, using gas. Let's get going."

No one was angry any more. Instead, a sort of strained friendliness had come into the air, indirect and placative. Even the old man was beginning to lift himself out of the chair. "Let me help, father," Eve said, but he pushed her away. "I can manage," he said sturdily. "I can manage. Just get me my coat, some one of you. I bet I'll be ready afore anybody."

Roy laughed awkwardly. "I bet you will too, Pop," he said.

"And you'll have such a nice time with old Mr. Wallis," Eve put in. "You know you always enjoy talking to him."

"Sure. Sure."

"Me, I still got to find my cap," Roy said, and Eve glanced at him.

"You really want to wear that old thing?" she demanded.

"I tell you, it's cold."

Eve smiled, not quite meeting his eyes. "Well, I know where it is," she said. "It's upstairs." She walked over to the door and then paused a moment, looking around the room—not looking at Roy or her father, but at the things in it, and not really seeing them either. "You help father out to the car," she said. "I'll find your cap for you."

*   *

He is a harmless old man!
Harmless—hell! . . .

DAMON RUNYON
My Father*

My Father is a Pioneer.

Of such an institution, Mr. N. Webster, who was himself something of a pioneer, says:

"Pioneer. One who goes before, as into the wilderness, preparing the way for others to follow."

I do not know that this description covers my father's case accurately—it sounds more like a word picture of a Frémont or a Pike, or an irrigation promoter, with little bearing upon a man who was the playmate of the untamed William Hickok, Mr. B. Masterson, and such; nevertheless, I have my father's word for it that he is a Pioneer.

His high-heeled boots have left their imprint upon the old cattle trails down Abilene and Dodge City way. I can picture in my mind's eye his small but hardy frame encased in the fringes fashionable at that day, cleaving a path toward the setting sun as he hotly pursued the elusive maverick and furrowed the pine bars of the Red Light and the Pink Dog Cafés of that interesting period with his hard-earned dollars.

I have a deep reverence for my father as a Pioneer, which is not shared by my wife Ellen.

She sees only, in that weatherbeaten little figure, an old gentleman with a tremendous capacity for indenting the cushions in the Brown Palace Hotel, where he forgathers at night with his ancient friends and talks in a loud and querulous tone of voice.

---

* This story first appeared in 1911, the year Damon Runyon's father died, but it is fiction. The elder Runyan (he spelled his name with an "a") was an itinerant printer-journalist who worked on newspapers all over the West in the period when that section was moving from frontier and pioneer life to stability. In *Runyon First and Last*, Clark Kinnaird describes Runyon's story as a "valedictory to his old man and the pioneers . . . a symbolic representation of the inevitable changes in American life."

My wife was born in the West at a time when department stores and nickelodeon theatres had crowded out the picturesque landscape to make room for a ragged skyline. Her father is not a Pioneer. He is merely the general superintendent of a railroad and travels in a private car. Her mother is not a Pioneer, either. She is a society leader.

Ellen, therefore, is inured to an atmosphere of labor difficulties and bargain sales, and could hardly be expected to sense the romance of the sunset trail as personified in a mild-looking little man with a stringy goatee, who declines to shake up the furnace on cold days. My father stands in proper awe of Ellen, and while he may raise his voice in a loud "I—remember—when" down at the Brown Palace, his tone is low and well modulated around my house, where he resides.

Understand, Ellen is not a shrew—far from it. Neither is she inclined to be peckish. She simply came into the world at a time when pioneerism had become a sort of misdemeanor, so far as six-pistols and wild Indians are concerned, and society felt it best to preserve a respectable silence regarding certain early days.

Also, my wife—but this does not go if she hears it—is very obtuse when it comes to an appreciation of the historical value of the notches in my father's gun. I myself know, from rumor and otherwise, that in his day my father was a man of parts, and his aim was esteemed along the border.

The Society of Pioneers decided to hold a reunion one summer, and for the purposes of that gathering they picked the old city of Trinity. There was method in this selection. The average Pioneer, like my father, has daughters-in-law and other women-folk holding receptions and functions about his family fireside, at which no account is taken of those hoary harbingers of civilization. Trinity is well removed from the social trail and is without reserve regarding the old days.

When my father announced his intention of attending the reunion, my wife offered no objection.

"Just so you ridiculous old men do your pioneering outside the city limits, I'll be satisfied," she remarked.

So my father, with patient resignation, packed his suit-case full of buckskin clothing and other odds and ends, and betook himself to Trinity, in company with a large number of other old gentlemen whose voices began to touch the highest pitch in the vocal scale as soon as the train moved them beyond the zone of home hostility.

When I returned that evening, I found Ellen in quite a state of mind.

"The Daughters of the Revolution have appointed me a member of a committee to go to Trinity and assist in dedicating a museum to the Spanish explorers," she announced. "I am to make a speech."

Personally, I have always felt that the son of a man who fought at 'Dobe Walls was as good as the great-great-granddaughter of a family who pitchforked Britons in the Lexington road, but I do not say so. I never shall, openly.

"Trinity? That's where father has gone," I said.

"Well," Ellen replied tartly, "those foolish old men haven't anything to do with this museum. This is being done by the Daughters, and as other members of the committee are taking their husbands, you can go with me."

"It will be quite a surprise to father to see us," I suggested.

I do not feel called upon to explain that the dedication of the museum might have been arranged to be coincident with the Pioneer reunion because of the connecting historical relation of the two events. I, a scion of the 'Dobe Walls, will never gratuitously offend any Daughter of the Revolution.

I did not see my father, but I heard of him as soon as I registered our names at the best hotel in Trinity, and urged the grizzled man doing duty as clerk to give us good rooms.

"Kivingson, hey?" he remarked, scrutinizing the register. "Any relation to Bill Kivingson?"

"My father's name is William Kivingson," I replied coldly. My wife sniffed one of the most disdainful sniffs.

"The son of ole Bill Kivingson can have anything I've got," replied the old man. "Me'n' Bill are pards; we useter raise hell together around Lamar. . . ."

"Jonas, let us go to our rooms," interrupted Ellen scornfully.

"Yore ole man's around town sum'eres," called the clerk, as we mounted the stairs.

Trinity is a small but enthusiastic town on the old Santa Fe trail, which preserves many of its old-time traditions and all of its saloons. It was humming with activity. The business houses and the streets were hung with bunting and beaming with hospitality, while grizzled men dotted the landscape freely. It appeared that there were really two celebrations—the Pioneers' reunion and the dedication of the museum, the latter designed by the women as a sort of antidote for the masculine gathering.

I soon discovered that, as the son of Bill Kivingson, I was a man of honor in those parts at that particular time. The clerk at the hotel took care to point me out in my capacity of Bill Kivingson's offspring; and my hand was cordially shaken by aging men with a violence that threatened my physical well-being.

Ellen was busied with the other members of the committee of the Daughters, arranging the program for the dedication, and I wandered about the town. My search was not an exhaustive one, as I did not care to encroach upon my father's vacation, and, in addition to my natural feelings, there *are* some places where a bank attaché cannot follow even a Pioneer parent.

As I went about, mingling with the queer crowds, I heard strange and disquieting rumors dealing with the personality and actions of one whom they called "Still Bill," who appeared to be a character of some vehemence.

"Still Bill's broke the faro bank over to the Blue Moose," announced an ancient exfrontiersman as he approached a group of bronzed old men at the hotel office that evening.

"Made 'em turn the box after he took out twenty-six hundred dollars!"

"That Bill's a gray wolf," replied a tall man with long, straight hair. There was admiration in his tone. "If Still Bill gets to going good, there will be some fun in this burg!"

"He's eyes-going fair enough right now," replied the bearer of the news. "I mind the time at Trail City when he cleaned out the whole blame town. It was bustin' the bank started him that time, too."

"Yes," put in another, "I rec'leck how he stood off the marshal and the en-tire pop'lation of Dodge City for two days an' nights."

"Well," said the messenger, "he's got that ol' cap'n'ball pistol —that ole forty-five howitzer—an' he was tunin' up some when I left. He useter be able to singe your eyelashes with that weepon at fifty yards."

At this point a fat, breathless gentleman who added locomotion with a manzanita cane, hobbled excitedly into the office.

"He's loose!" panted this latest courier, in a quavering voice. "Ole Still Bill has done ontied himself! He's raisin' hell and puttin' a plug under ear over at the Moose! Like as not he'll come a-bulgin' down this street pretty quick. I'm goin' home!"

"He useter be a long-winded cuss, too," said someone. "I don't reckon at his age, he can hold out more'n two days, but I seen the time when a week wasn't no limit!"

"They's been a-many a-ring-tailed, red-eyed son o' trouble turned loose in these here parts," quavered the courier. "I seen 'em come and I seen 'em go, but they's never been no white man could claw within a foot o' the neck o' ole Bill Kivingson!"

Kivingson! Bill Kivingson! *My Father!*

I approached the group. "Gentlemen," said I, "you surely do not mean Mr. William Kivingson—a smallish man with a goatee and . . . ?"

"Still Bill? That's *him!*" came in full chorus.

"Why," said I, "it—it isn't possible that he should be performing actions such as you speak of! He is a harmless old man!"

"Harmless-*hell!*" snorted the fat old Pioneer. "Harmless like a mess o' rattlesnakes!"

"But I'm his son!" I argued.

"I don't give a hoo-raw who you are! I'm his pal and I *know* Still Bill Kivingson—knowed him before you was born. It's goodnight, all, fer me!"

Now of course my natural thought was to go and get my father and make him retire for the night; but the hotel clerk laid a kind restraining hand upon my arm.

"Lay off o' him, son," he said. "When Still Bill gits a-goin', you jest got to give him a clean track and keep well under kivver. I ain't seen him speed none in twenty years, but I know what he *could* do. Jest you go to bed and lay off o' him.

"He won't hurt nobody," he continued. "All the old-timers'll keep out of his way, and he never did kill no bartenders, or such, in his life, because he needs 'em. Don't you worry about him. It's just them animile sperrits which has been plugged up fer a long time, coming out an' sniffin' around. O' course, if he should happen to think o' somebody he don't like, he might bother 'em some; but they ain't no one about Trinity he ain't made up with long ago."

I debated the matter in my mind and came to the conclusion that I had better follow the clerk's advice. Who was I, that I should obstruct the course of a hero of the 'Dobe Walls, equipped with a cap and ball?

I lay awake for several hours, the tumult of the street pouring in at my window. Occasionally I heard above the hum of voices a pistol shot, which never failed to produce deep silence—after a great shuffling of feet. The pedestrians seemed to be seeking shelter. In the hush which followed these explosions there would come a voice, uplifted in warlike declamation. I could not make out the words, but there seemed to be a familiar ring to the belligerent chant.

When I went down the stairs the next morning, leaving Ellen at her toilet, a strange sight presented itself. It was nine o'clock. Outside, the sun was shining from a turquoise sky, and the air was soft as down, yet the lobby of the hotel was packed with men and women who stood gazing through the windows upon that scene of peace and quiet as if a terrible storm raged without.

Across the street, I could see, the stores were filled with similar crowds. The streets were deserted. An old man disengaged himself from the throng and sidled over to me. It was the hotel clerk.

"Son," said he, "I don't like fer to tell you-all, but yore ole man, Still Bill, he's a-goin' good and strong this mornin'. He's plum' busted this celebration, which it can't go on with him a-streamin' up and down the streets like a pestilence. He's a-holdin' forth down yonder at the Moose, an' every now an' then he comes a-boilin' up this way to see if they's any defenseless folks he can devastate. Son, yore dad is a wolf—a curly wolf, that's all—and time don't change him none."

"He certainly is a long-winded ole body," declared another. "I reckon it's his superflus energy o' twenty year a-bubbin' out all to onct. He allows he has decided to postpone the parade an' celebration until tomorrow and that he ain't goin' to permit no moosee dedication a-a-a-tall. He ain't decided yet whether he'll move this town plum' away or not."

At that moment a high treble yell smote the air, and the

crowd swayed back from the windows. I peered outside to see, far down the street, a small figure rocketing along at amazing speed. Clad in buckskins, feathered at the hems, a wide hat, it gave him the appearance of an animated mushroom, and waving a long-barreled revolver, my father surged along in a billow of sound. While I watched, shamefaced, some of his expressions came to my ears.

"I'm a howlin' wolf from ole Mizzou, an' I'm a-huntin' gore!" he bawled. "I picks my teeth with bowie-knives, an' the bark o' six-guns is music to my ears! Yee-owo-wow! I'm a snake in the grass, an' I hiss when you pass, an' I'm searchin' for folks to eat! Wow!"

He had a clear path, and he swirled along the street for a block or two, then doubled back and disappeared in a vocal storm.

"Ain't he a bear?" inquired the hotel clerk; and I could see that among these Pioneers my father's exhibitions, however much it shamed me, had aroused considerable admiration.

"Has he hurt anybody?" I inquired nervously.

"*Hurt* 'em, son?" said the hotel clerk. "*Hurt* 'em? Boy, they ain't anybody get near enough to ole Hell-on-Wheels out there to let him *hurt* 'em. He never *hurts* no one if he gits 'em. He jest KILLS 'em. An' he ain't bin able for to ketch no one here."

"Has he been going all night long?"

"All night," replied the clerk. "He ain't paused for drink for man or beast to date. An' bimeby we're goin' to set a bear trap out there in the street so business can proceed. Sim Leggins has gone after the trap now. Sim is the authorities, an' a pussonal friend o' yer dad's, but he's decided Still Bill has got his twenty years' worth."

Beyond the shadow of a doubt I should shortly have nerved myself to going after my father—there is no question in my mind but that I should have done it; but while I was steeling myself, my wife appeared—my wife, the immaculate Ellen, appeared in the crowded lobby, clad in a Japanese kimono, her hair in curl-papers.

"What is this I hear?" she demanded. "The members of my committee tell me that our dedication is being postponed by some beast of a man—what does this mean?"

I had not the heart to tell her that it was my father. I could never have found the heart to do so. But at that moment he disclosed his identity by reappearing in the street—gun in hand and a yell in his throat.

Again he careened past the hotel, the crowd falling back dismayed—and as I stood there, the picture of embarrassment, if nothing more, my wife edged close to the window and stared.

"Come back, Ellen, dear," I said. "They say he's very dangerous to people he does not like."

That was an unfortunate slip. I had never before suggested that my father did not like my wife—certainly he had never intimated such a thing.

"Yee-ow-wow!" yelled my father, as he swung back toward his Blue Moose retreat and disappeared.

My wife hurriedly left the hotel in a flutter of Japanese coloring, and with a toss of bedroom headgear. The crowd gasped. She was heading straight for the door of the Blue Moose. I followed—I have never permitted my wife to go where I do not go myself—and the crowd trailed along, nervously.

At the door of the Blue Moose saloon I paused, my heart beating with grave concern.

Imagine my feelings! My beloved wife, unappreciative of the danger attached to an eruption of twenty years of repressed pioneerial fervor, mindful only of the jeopardy of social standing, had flung herself headlong into the arms of Peril.

And my beloved father was Peril!

About me pressed the faces of the people, gray with apprehension, each head bent toward the door of the Blue Moose in a listening attitude.

Shortly I should have plunged through those doors regardless of consequences; shortly I should have rushed to my obvious duty.

From the interior of the Blue Moose arose a voice—a woman's voice—the voice of Ellen, my wife.

The door suddenly flew open with a bang, scattering the crowd like frightened sheep. My wife appeared. In one hand she held a long cap-and-ball revolver. In the other she clasped the left ear of a meek old gentleman, who was very white as to face, and who rubbed his hands together nervously.

"At your time of life, too!" my wife was saying. "You ought to be ashamed of yourself, you silly old man!"

The crowd collected itself again, amazed, startled.

"Now, Elly—" quavered my father.

"Hush!" she ordered, in tones such as I never wish to hear again. "Not another word, you ridiculous old man!"

And up the street, now teaming with an astounded multitude, she led the resentless howl wolf and snake in the grass, while I, who seemed destined always to be in the rear of the procession, followed, still harassed by emotion.

"I'm going to lock you up in a closet until the next train leaves," my wife was saying. "You—"

"Don't lose my gun, Elly," my father exhorted humbly. "It's the one with notches on it."

A little boy, perhaps ten years of age, was running along beside them, whooping shrilly.

"Here, boy!" said Ellen, pushing the famous revolver into the youngster's hands. "Here's a nice plaything for you!"

"And now, ladies and gentlemen," said my wife, in closing her brief remarks at the dedication of the museum, "it is with a feeling of deepest reverence toward the wonderful men of that early period, and to those equally wonderful men who came at a later day to develop and perpetuate the path of progress that we dedicate this small monument in the hope that it will ever keep green the memory of the Spanish explorers and the American Pioneer!"

I have a high regard for my father as a Pioneer, which is not shared by my wife, Ellen.

*   *

. . . I woke up and couldn't get my breath. . . .

JOHN UPDIKE

from

PACKED DIRT, CHURCH GOING,
A DYING CAT, A TRADED CAR

. . . I HAD FORGOTTEN how grand Alton hospital was. I had not seen its stately entrance, approached down a grassy mall bright with the first flush of green, since, at the age of seven, I had left the hospital unburdened of my tonsils. Then, too, it had been spring, and my mother was with me. I recalled it to her, and she said, "I felt so guilty. You were so sick."

"Really? I remember it as so pleasant." They had put a cup of pink rubber over my nose and there had been a thunderous flood of the smell of cotton candy and I opened my eyes and my mother was reading a magazine beside my bed.

"You were such a hopeful boy," my mother said, and I did not look at her face for fear of seeing her crying.

I wondered aloud if a certain girl in my high school class was still a nurse here.

"Oh, dear," my mother said. "Here I thought you came all this way to see your poor old father and all you care about is seeing—" And she used the girl's maiden name, though the girl had been married as long as I had.

Within the hospital, she surprised me by knowing the way. Usually, wherever we went, it was my father or I who knew the way. As I followed her through the linoleum maze, my mother's shoulders seemed already to have received the responsible shawl of widowhood. Like the halls of a palace, the hospital corridors were lined with patient petitioners. Negro girls electrically dramatic in their starched white uniforms folded bales of cotton sheets; gray men pushed wrung mops. We went through an Exit sign, down a stairway, into a realm where gaunt convalescents in bathrobes shuffled in and out of doorways. I saw my father diagonally through a doorway before we entered his room. He was sitting up in bed, supported sultanlike by a wealth of pillows and clad in red-striped pajamas.

I had never seen him in pajamas before; a great man for the shortest distance between two points, he slept in his underclothes. But, having been at last captured in pajamas, like a big-hearted lion he did not try to minimize his humiliation, but lay fully exposed, without a sheet covering even his feet. Bare, they looked pale, gentle, and oddly unused.

Except for a sullen lymphatic glow under his cheeks, his face was totally familiar. I had been afraid that his loss of faith would show, like the altered shape of his mouth after he had had all his teeth pulled. With grins we exchanged the shy handshake that my going off to college had forced upon us. I sat on the window sill by his bed, my mother took the chair at the foot of the bed, and my father's roommate, a tanned and fortyish man flat on his back with a crushed vertebra, sighed and blew smoke toward the ceiling and tried, I suppose, not to hear us. Our conversation, though things were radically changed, followed old patterns. Quite quickly the talk shifted from him to me. "I don't know how you do it, David," he said. "I couldn't do what you're doing if you paid me a million dollars a day." Embarrassed and flattered, as usual, I tried to shush him, and he disobediently turned to his roommate and called loudly, "I don't know where the kid gets his ideas. Not from his old man, I know that. I never gave that poor kid an idea in my life."

"Sure you did," I said softly, trying to take pressure off the man with the painful back. "You taught me two things. Always butter bread toward the edges because enough gets in the middle anyway, and No matter what happens to you, it'll be a new experience."

To my dismay, this seemed to make him melancholy. "That's right, David," he said. "No matter what happens to you, it'll be a new experience. The only thing that worries me is that *she*" —he pointed at my mother—"will crack up the car. I don't want anything to happen to your mother."

"The car, you mean," my mother said, and to me she added, "It's a sin, the way he worships that car."

My father didn't deny it. "Jesus I love that car," he said. "It's the first car I've ever owned that didn't go bad on me. Remember all those heaps we used to ride back and forth in?"

The old Chevy was always getting dirt in the fuel pump and refusing to start at awkward hours. Once, going down Fire Hill, the left front wheel had broken off the axle; my father wrestled with the steering wheel while the tires screamed and the white posts of the guard fence floated calmly toward my eyes. When the car slid sideways to a stop just short of the embankment my father's face was stunned and the corners of his mouth dribbled saliva. I was surprised; it had not occurred to me to be frightened. The '36 Buick had drunk oil, a quart every fifty miles, and loved to have flat tires after midnight, when I would be gliding home with a scrubbed brain and the smell of lipstick in my nose. Once, when we had both gone into town and I had dropped him off and taken the car, I had absent-mindedly driven home alone. I came in the door and my mother said, "Why, where's your father?"

My stomach sank. "My Lord," I said, "I forgot I had him!"

As, smiling, I took in breath and prepared to dip with him into reminiscence of these adventures, my father, staring stonily into the air above his pale and motionless toes, said, "I love this place. There are a lot of wonderful gentlemen in here. The only thing that worries me is that mother will crack up the car."

To my horror I saw that my mother, leaning forward red-faced in the chair at the foot of the bed, was silently crying. He glanced at her and said to me, "It's a funny feeling. The night before we went to see the doctor, I woke up and couldn't get my breath and realized I wasn't ready to die. I had always thought I would be. It's a funny feeling."

"Luckily for your dad," "all his faith," "wonderful gentlemen"; these phrases were borne in on me with a dreadful weight and my tongue seemed pressed flat on the floor of its grave. The pajama stripes under my eyes stirred and streamed, real blood. I wanted to speak, to say how I needed him and to beg him not to leave me, but there were no words, no form of words available in our tradition. . . .

*   *

When you were very young it was my delight to play with you all, and I think with a sigh that such days can never return.

CHARLES DARWIN

*   *

. . . he loved and was loved. . . .

MAX LERNER
My Father "Moved"

MY FATHER DIED on Saturday, as gently and peacefully as he had lived, and he was buried yesterday. At eighty-seven he had lived beyond the Biblical assignment, yet even an old man leaves a gaping hole when he breaks through the skein of life and hurtles into no-being.

As I stood at his grave, listening to the service that has come down through the centuries, my mind wound back through the corridors of his life. He came of a line of scholars, men of the Book, simple folk who warmed themselves by the lamps of the past and gloried in the exploits and tragedies of their people.

In Russia he had studied at a *yeshiva*, and traveled from village to village as an itinerant scholar. But Czarist society was stifling. My father and his young wife wanted a chance to earn something, and wanted their children to breathe a freer air and become someone. At thirty-three, in 1903, he came to New York as part of the great migration of the century, and my mother followed in 1907 with her four children. He went through the familiar immigrant odyssey: He was a small peddler, worked in a garment loft, became a Hebrew teacher, turned to farming and failed at it, tried a milk delivery route, became a small grocer. Finally he went back to what he loved—his work as a Hebrew teacher, keeping at it until a few years before his death.

His was one of the millions of American stories that have woven the history of this country. Life was not easy for my father. He had disappointments, frustrations, tragedies. He was never a big success at anything, nor did he make a great noise in the world. But he loved and was loved, and he had joy in his children. Had he stayed behind in Europe he and they would long ago have been ashes at Auschwitz or ciphers in a Soviet ant-society.

When I saw him toward the end of his illness, while he could still talk, he asked me to bring his notebooks. They were a confusion of ledgers, journals, loose sheets, on which over the years he had written his reflections on a variety of themes, covering his life within the world outside, dealing with the early prophets and the latter-day secular figures, with Hitler and Stalin and Nasser, Roosevelt and Truman, Weizmann and Ben-Gurion.

I am, alas, an ignorant man. With all my years of schooling I am unable to read the languages in which my father wrote, as my sons are already able to read mine. I shall save the bundle of pages on which he spent the burden of his hours, driven as he was by a strange necessity to find a garment for what he felt and dreamt.

Some day I may repair my ignorance and discover what thoughts they were that coursed through the mind of this patient, reflective man.

His killer—the killer of so many—was cancer. Mercifully, once it struck it did its work fast. In his last few days he was unconscious.

I think I was the last person whom he saw and recognized. When he whispered my name, I felt a stab of the fitness of it. Surely it is a good thing for a father, in his final moments of consciousness, to know that his son is near him. The father-son relation is the basic link of continuity in life, carrying the male principle and the tradition of responsibility from one generation to the next.

The need for a father is as crucial as the need for a son, and the search of each for the other—through all the days of one's life—exempts no one. Happy is the man who finds both.

My father was a gentle and permissive man. When I think of him I think of the lines of the great E. E. Cummings poem:

> My father moved through dooms of love
> Through sames of am through haves of give,
> Singing each morning out of each night
> My father moved through depths of height . . .
> Because my father lived his soul
> Love is the whole and more than all.

Death seems all the more pitiless when it comes to these gentle people. When I last saw my father, just before he died, he seemed so shrunken and wasted that I fear I broke down shamelessly and wept. It was for more than my father that I wept. It was for death which shows up the final helplessness of life, and for the crazy tragic absurdity of the whole human condition.

And then, along with the other mourners, I heard and spoke the thundering syllables of the great *Kaddish—Yisgadal V'yiskadash Sh'me Rabbo,** and I looked at the little huddle of my father's friends of many years who stood around, and the absurdity became a little less absurd. Even the most rational of us must admit that there is a healing power in the ritual words when you face what reason cannot fathom.

I keep thinking of my father's last words to me. I had been sitting by his side while he slept. Then my father moved a bit, and his eyes half opened. I bent close to him, and barely made out his whispered words. "They are calling from Zion," he said.

It is a good belief with which to die.

---

* "Magnified and sanctified be His great name . . . ," the first words of an age-old prayer affirming faith in the continuation of life.